VIETNAMESE
LEGENDS

VIETNAMESE LEGENDS

Adapted from the Vietnamese by

George F. Schultz

CHARLES E. TUTTLE COMPANY
RUTLAND, VERMONT & TOKYO, JAPAN

Representatives
For Continental Europe:
BOXER BOOKS INC. Zurich

For the British Isles:
PRENTICE-HALL INTERNATIONAL, INC. London

For Australasia
PAUL FLESCH & CO., PTY. LTD. Melbourne

Published by the Charles E. Tuttle Company Inc.
of Rutland, Vermont & Tokyo, Japan
with editorial offices at
Suido 1-chome, 2–6, Bunkyo-ku, Tokyo, Japan

Copyright in Japan, 1965
by Charles E. Tuttle Co. Inc.

Library of Congress Catalog Card No. 65–25634

First Printing 1965

Book design and typography by John Paull
PRINTED IN JAPAN

 CONTENTS

DEDICATED
to the
Vietnamese people
and
Vietnamese-American
friendship

 PREFACE

BY VINH HUYEN

President, Board of Directors Vietnamese-American Association

The author of "Vietnamese Legends" Mr. George F. Schultz, was Executive Director of the Vietnamese-American Association during the years 1956–58. Mr. Schultz was responsible for the construction of the present Vietnamese-American Center in Saigon and for the development of the cultural and educational program of the Association.

Shortly after his arrival in Vietman, Mr. Schultz began to study the language, literature, and history of Vietnam and was soon recognized as an authority, not only by his fellow Americans, for it was his duty to brief them in these subjects, but by many Vietnamese as well. He has published papers entitled "The Vietnamese Language" and "Vietnamese Names" as well as an English translation of the *Cung-Oan ngam-khuc,* "The Plaints of an Odalisque."

9

It was my privilege to be president of the Board of Directors of the Vietnamese-American Association during the time that Mr. Schultz was the Executive Director, and it is a great pleasure for me to have a small part in presenting "Vietnamese Legends" to the public.

Saigon

FOREWORD

This collection of Vietnamese legends was begun during my tour in Saigon as Director of the Vietnamese-American Association, a bi-national center sponsored by the United States Information Agency. A subsequent world tour and other assignments have delayed publication until the present time.

My position as Executive director of the Association brought me into intimate contact with the Vietnamese people at all levels. It was my first experience in Southeast Asia, and I had much to learn. I found the Vietnamese to be a friendly and hospitable people of a modest and retiring disposition. They prize erudition and I found that I could best gain their respect by learning something of their language, literature, and civilization. This was not a simple task for at that time little had appeared in English about the cultural aspects of Vietnam; *Viet-My,* the journal of the Vietnamese-American Association, served and continues to serve a good cause in this respect.

The Vietnamese are a very old race, and legend takes them back to the year 2,879 B.C., when they were supposedly living in the valley of the upper Yangtse River. Over the centuries they moved from that region to the south of China. Their historical period begins in the third century B.C., when they are found in the Red River delta, in what is now North Vietnam. After several centuries of independence, they were subjugated by the powerful Chinese and only in A.D. 939 were they able to gain independence again. After that they moved south by land and by sea, reaching the southern extremity of what is now Vietnam in 1774.

Vietnamese language, literature, and civilization owe a great deal to the Chinese. It would be wrong, however, to say that the Vietnamese have slavishly imitated their northern neighbors; on the Chinese base, there has developed a language, literature, and civilization of distinct Vietnamese flavor.

A great many Chinese myths, fables, and legends have been passed on to the Vietnamese; others are of purely Vietnamese origin. "The Story of Tam and Cam" will be recognized as the Vietnamese version of the Chinese Cinderella story. (It may surprise Western readers to learn that the first Cinderella was Chinese). This Chinese aspect of their culture does not bother the Vietnamese in the least, although there is presently very little *rapport* between the two peoples.

Among my Vietnamese friends who have aided in the preparation of this collection, I should like to mention the names of Mrs. Nguyen Ngoc Lang, Mrs. L. T. Bach Lan, Mr. Pham Duy Khiem, Mr. Do Vang Ly, Mr. Nguyen Phu Doc, and Mr. Le Huy Hap.

Columbia City,
Indiana, U.S.A.

GEORGE F. SCHULTZ

1

HOW THE TIGER GOT HIS STRIPES

T HIS STORY took place in prehistoric times, when animals still had the power of speech.

A young farmer had just stopped plowing his rice paddy. It was noon, and he sat down to eat his lunch in the shade of a banana plant near his land.

Not far away his water buffalo was grazing along the grass-covered dikes enclosing the rice fields. After the meal the farmer reclined and observed the stout beast which was chewing quietly. From time to time it would chase away the obnoxious flies with a vigorous swing of its massive head.

Suddenly the great beast became alarmed; the wind carried the odor of a dangerous animal. The buffalo rose to its feet, and awaited the arrival of the enemy.

With the speed of lightning a tiger sprang into the clearing.

"I have not come as an enemy," he said. "I only wish to have something explained. I have been watching you every day from the edge of the forest, and I have observed the strange spectacle of your common labor with the man. That man, that small and vertical being, who has neither great strength nor sharp vision, nor even a keen sense of smell, has been able to keep you in bondage and work you for his profit. You are actually ten times heavier than he, much stronger, and more hardened to heavy labor. Yet he rules you. What is the source of his magic power?"

"To tell the truth," said the buffalo, "I know nothing about all that. I only know I shall never be freed of his power, for he has a talisman he calls wisdom."

"I must ask him about that," said the tiger, "because, you see, if I could get this wisdom I would have even greater power over the other animals. Instead of having to conceal myself and spring on them unawares, I could simply order them to remain motionless. I could choose from among all the animals, at my whim and fancy, the most delicious meats."

"Well!" replied the startled buffalo. "Why don't you ask the farmer about his wisdom."

The tiger decided to approach the farmer.

"Mr. Man," he said, "I am big, strong, and quick but I want to be more. I have heard it said that you have something called wisdom which makes it possible for you to rule over all the animals. Can you transfer this wisdom to me? It would be of great value to me in my daily search for food."

VIETNAMESE LEGENDS

"Unfortunately," replied the man, "I have left my wisdom at home. I never bring it with me to the fields. But, if you like I will go there for it."

"May I accompany you?" asked the tiger, delighted with what he had just heard.

"No, you had better remain here," replied the farmer, "if the villagers see you with me they may become alarmed and perhaps beat you to death. Wait here. I will find what you need and return."

And the farmer took a few steps, as if to set off homeward. But then he turned around and with wrinkled brow addressed the tiger.

"I am somewhat disturbed by the possibility that during my absence you might be seized with the desire to eat my buffalo. I have great need of it in my daily work. Who would repay me for such a loss?"

The tiger did not know what to say.

The farmer continued: "If you consent, I will tie you to a tree; then my mind will be free."

The tiger wanted the mysterious wisdom very much —so much, in fact, that he was willing to agree to anything. He permitted the farmer to pass ropes round his body and to tie him to the trunk of a big tree.

The farmer then went home and gathered a great armload of dry straw. He returned to the big tree and placed the straw under the tiger and set it on fire.

"Behold my wisdom!" he shouted at his unfortunate victim, as the flames encircled the tiger and burned him fiercely.

The tiger roared so loudly that the neighboring

HOW THE TIGER GOT HIS STRIPES

trees trembled. He raged and pleaded, but the farmer would not untie him.

Finally the fire burned through the ropes and he was able to free himself from cremation. He bounded away into the forest, howling with pain.

18

In time his wounds healed, but he was never able to rid himself of the long black stripes of the ropes which the flames had seared into his flesh.

THE SUPERNATURAL CROSSBOW

THIS IS a legend taken from the ancient Chronicles. More than 2,300 years ago the king of the realm of Thuc sought to marry a princess from the house of the Hong Bang, which was reigning in the kingdom of Van Lang. Embittered by the refusal that he received, he swore the ruin of the Hong Bang; but he died without satisfying his hatred, leaving the task to his descendants.

This was the origin of the continual wars between the kingdoms of Thuc and Van Lang.

For many years the Hong Bang were victorious. But powerful in their success and certain of the protection of the genii, they relaxed their vigilance and lived in idleness and indolence. Their enemy, Thuc Phan, a king of the realm of Thuc, began a long series of military preparations; he chose the right moment to invade Van Lang and crushed the Hong Bang.

*　　*　　*

Thuc Phan united the two kingdoms of Thuc and Van Lang under the name of Au Lac and took the name of An Duong Vuong for himself. He established his capital in the territory of Phong Khe. Desirous of protecting his realm against the bandits of the north, he ordered a mighty wall to be built at the northern extremity of his capital. But as soon as the wall was finished, a violent storm broke out and rain poured down in torrents. A strong wind howled and roared until the wall fell with a deafening crash.

An Duong Vuong rebuilt the wall three times; but as soon as it was completed, it was destroyed again in the same way.

At last a council of ministers was called; one minister, more clever than the others, arose and bowed.

"Will the Son of Heaven be pleased to hear my humble opinion?" he asked. "Since the wall has been destroyed so many times in the same way, it must be that the gods are against us. Let us attempt to appease them by erecting an altar and making sacrifices to ask them for advice and help."

This suggestion met with general approval. Accordingly, the king ordered the erection of an altar on the river bank outside the Eastern Gate. Cows and buffaloes were sacrificed and prayers were said. The king himself fasted for three days and nights and prostrated himself for hours before the altar, asking for guidance.

On the seventh day of the third month, a genie in the shape of an enormous golden tortoise appeared to the king in a dream and spoke in a human voice.

"Son of Heaven," he said, "your prayers have been heard by the gods, who have been pleased to send me here to help you." Then the tortoise instructed him in the proper way to build the wall. "This is a land of rivers and mountains, populated by spirits; the spirits of the mountains have caused your wall to crumble," he continued, "for they are very mischievous and like to play tricks on human beings to show their power."

When the king awoke the next morning, he remembered all that the tortoise had told him. He followed instructions exactly and built a great wall of fortifications in the form of a sea shell or conch. He called it Co Loa and the capital became known as Co Loa Tanh, or the "City of the Conch."

An Duong Vuong now felt that his wall would resist the elements and that his city was secure. But he also realized that he was surrounded by powerful enemies and that he might not always be able to defend it.

The golden tortoise understood his doubts and again appeared to him in his sleep.

"Prosperity or misfortune depends on the will of Heaven," he said, "but if men are deserving, Heaven will aid them. Since you manifest such great confidence in me, I will make you a present of one of my claws, which you can use as a trigger for your crossbow. It will drive away evil spirits and it will even defeat an entire army in battle. But never forget that the ultimate

THE SUPERNATURAL CROSSBOW

safety of your realm depends on your vigilance." The tortoise pulled off one of his claws and entrusted it to the king; he then returned to the river and disappeared.

The king was very happy when he awoke and found the magic claw in his hand. He ordered a precious crossbow to be made with the magic claw as trigger, and a beautiful crystal case was made to contain the crossbow. The king was very grateful to the tortoise, for now he firmly believed his realm would enjoy peace and order for many years.

At that time China was under the rule of the powerful Emperor Shih Huang of the Ch'in dynasty; Shih Huang had conquered all his feudal neighbors and his armies reached to the South Sea. In the same year that An Duong Vuong began the Great Wall, he sent a great army of men and horses down from southern China to conquer the Kingdom of Au Lac. But this army was flung back time after time and was finally destroyed by the magic crossbow, before it even approached Co Loa Thanh.

Three years later Shih Huang sent forth another army, 500,000 strong, under the leadership of the great General Trieu Da and the northern part of Au Lac easily fell into Chinese hands. The Chinese hordes came in three sections—on horse, on foot, and by boat; they came with flags floating in the air, forests of weapons clashing together, and fierce-looking officers riding forward on their foaming steeds. Trieu Da deployed his troops on the Mountain of the Rusty Axe, his junks on the river, and besieged the capital.

King An Duong Vuong watched calmly from a window of his citadel as the three sections poured on towards Co Loa Thanh like a powerful swarm of ants. Then he walked to the ramparts, taking with him the magic crossbow with the holy tortoise's claw, and fired three arrows at the multitude of enemy soldiers. Twang! 10,000 Chinese soldiers fell like dry leaves; with the second arrow another 10,000 fell, and with the third arrow, another 10,000.

The remainder of the army retreated in panic.

Trieu Da was too ashamed and afraid to return to give his emperor an account of his defeat. Incapable of fighting against a supernatural weapon, he decided to master An Duong Vuong deceitfully; he pretended to make peace with him by sending his son, Trong Thuy, to the royal court as a hostage, to indicate his desire for friendly relations. The king received the latter in good faith; he was even generous enough to extend his friendship to the young man, admitting him to his entourage and giving him his only daughter, Princess My Chau, in marriage. He gave Trieu Da a large county situated north of the Bang Giang as his special province.

* * *

Trong Thuy loved his wife, and for a time the newly wed couple lived in perfect happiness. The young princess was charm itself, and Trong Thury adored her. Yet in his heart he never forgot the secret mission with which he had been entrusted, and secretly vowed to help his father conquer Au Lac at some future date.

THE SUPERNATURAL CROSSBOW

Trong Thuy coaxed and cajoled his innocent wife, beseeching her to let him see the miraculous crossbow; she yielded in the end and showed it to him. He examined it carefully and made a false claw. He then stole the holy claw and replaced it with the false one.

One day Trong Thuy requested An duong Vuong's permission to go home to visit his parents. To Princess My Chau he explained that conjugal love should not cause one to neglect one's duty towards one's parents.

It had been a long time since he had protracted himself before them and he regretted that he could not take her with him; the route to the Northern territories was long, and it passed through forests and mountains infested with bandits.

Princess My Chau flung herself on the ground before him and clung to his feet. "Please do not go away, my lord," she implored. "Is this unhappy person to be alone for months, perhaps for years? There are so many lofty mountains and deep valleys which separate our two countries. Who knows what might happen to my lord during such a long and dangerous journey? How can I restrain my tears at the prospect of such a long separation? The Cowherd and the Spinning Maid in heaven meet across the Milky Way once a year, but shall we ever meet again?" And the princess wept more bitterly than ever.

"Does this weeping become the Most Worshipful Daughter of the Dragon." asked Trong Thuy, trying to sooth her feelings. "Of course your unworthy servant will come back to you, and then we shall live together as happily as before."

But the princess would not stop weeping, for she had a foreboding of some great misfortune. "Would my lord please remember his gift of a broacaded winter coat lined with goose down," she said in tears. "Our love is imperishable, but the peace of nations is often ephemeral; if ever a war occurs between our countries, I will scatter the down at the crossroads to show you the way I have taken."

At the moment of separation, Trong Thuy was filled with a strange emotion. His wife, in her love and confidence in him, had unconsciously betrayed her father and country.

The separation was heart-rending; after many bitter tears and vows of love and devotion, he left with an unbearable pain in his heart, for he loved the princess and had to betray her ignominiously for the sake of his father and his country.

* * *

Trong Thuy then rejoined his father and gave him the holy claw. Trieu Da was overjoyed, and at once led a strong army across the land to Au Lac.

The sunlight glittered on the lances and spurs of the Chinese soldiers and their multicolored banners fluttered in the wind.

The army wound its way out of the land of Tan like a gigantic snake, and the beating of the war drums resounded in the distance like thunder.

THE SUPERNATURAL CROSSBOW

An Duong Vuong and his daughter were playing chess when the tower watchman entered and flung himself at their feet.

"Son of Heaven and Daughter of the Dragon, the enemy is coming!"

"Let them come!" said the king, roaring with laughter at the thought of these bold and foolish men coming to meet certain death. "Have no fear, my beloved daughter, the magic crossbow will again work miracles."

And he let the enemy approach without going forth to meet them; nor did he give orders for the defense of the capital. When the sentry from the summit of the ramparts reported that the Chinese hordes obscured the horizon, he was content to say:

"Has my neighbor forgotten the magic crossbow?"

And he continued the game of chess.

When the enemy was at the very gates of Co Loa Thanh, the king arose and aimed the crossbow. But after the first shot he realized he had been betrayed. He fired again and again, but the enemy continued to flow forward like a devastating flood.

Deciding to escape, An Duong Vuong barely had time to mount his horse, bringing My Chau up behind him.

They galloped swiftly to the South, leaving An Duong Vuong's capital and kingdom behind them.

They rode past many field and marshes, and as they approached the crossroads, My Chau left a trial of goose down so that Trong Thuy might follow.

Back at the palace, Trong Thuy perceived that the king and his daughter had fled, and immediately gave chase. Guided by traces of down, he was not long in picking up their trail.

An Duong Vuong crossed plains and forests like a tornado; he scaled hills, cascaded down slopes, and crossed rivers. Each time he slowed the pace, he would hear the gallop of his pursuer. Then he would spur his horse anew, and the wild flight would begin again.

On went the king's horse, carrying them farther and farther away, until at last they came to a great sea. Not a boat was to be seen and it was apparent that there was no way to cross. The king lifted his face to the sky and cried in despair:

"O gods, have you forsaken me? And you, Holy Tortoise, where are you in my hour of need?"

Out of the deep blue sea arose the golden tortoise and cried in a powerful voice:

"Beware of the treacherous enemy who sits behind you."

The king turned around in his saddle and gazed at the princess. My Chau shivered like a leaf in a storm and large tears rolled down her cheeks.

While the princess looked at him imploringly, An Duong Vuong grasped a dagger and stabbed her ruthlessly in the heart. Then drawing his great sword, he cut off her head.

Filled with horror at his shameful deed, the king followed the golden tortoise into the storm-tossed waters, and disappeared.

THE SUPERNATURAL CROSSBOW

When Trong Thuy arrived at the scene and discovered the severed body of My Chau, his anguish knew no bounds. Shedding bitter tears he gathered up the fragile body and carried it back to the capital for burial.

One day, unable to bear his grief any longer Trong Thuy threw himself into the deep pond where My Chau had loved to bathe. In this way his soul would go to the other world with the one he had loved.

The blood that flowed from the princess' body was washed away by the rolling sea and absorbed by the many oysters of that shore. Since that time they have produced many beautiful pearls, and legend has it that these pearls became more brilliant when dipped into the pond where Trong Thuy drowned himself.

The reputation of the pond water spread as far as China, and the emperor demanded that a vase containing the liquid be added to the triennial tribute.

* * *

Today we can see a small temple on a mountain near the seashore where Princess My Chau met her death. But it is particularly at Co Loa Thanh, the Ancient City of the Conch, that tradition keeps alive the cult of An Duong Vuong and My Chau. There, in the sanctuary of the temple, a flame has burned for 2000 years before the tablet of heroes who have fought for national independence. Farther on, a sacred banyan tree, several centuries old, covers the humble altar of Princess My Chau.

3

LITTLE
STATESMAN LY

THERE WAS once a famous Vietnamese statesman whose name was Ly. He was very short of
stature; in fact, he was so short that the top of
his head was no higher than a man's waist.

Statesman Ly was sent to China to settle a very important political problem with that nation. When the
Emperor of China looked down from his Dragon
Throne and saw this little man, he exclaimed, "Are
the Vietnamese such little people?"

Ly answered: "Sire, in Vietnam, we have both little
men and big men. Our ambassadors are chosen in
accordance with the importance of the problem. As
this is a small matter, they have sent me to negotiate.
When there is a big problem between us, we will send
a big man to speak with you."

The Emperor of China pondered: "If the Vietnamese

consider this important problem only a small matter, they must indeed be a great and powerful people."

 So he lessened his demands and the matter was settled then and there.

4

THE
BUFFALO BOY
AND THE
BANYAN TREE

CUOI WAS of a very, very poor family. He had no education and the only job he could get was that of buffalo boy for a rich farmer. Every day he would look after the water buffaloes in the rice fields, prepare food for the pigs, and collect firewood in the forest. For these tasks the farmer gave him food and clothing and enough money to live on.

One day, while gathering wood in the forest far from home, Cuoi came upon a tiger cub that was frolicking in the sun. He picked up the cub intending to have some sport with it. As he did so, he heard a frightful growl from a nearby thicket. It was the mother of the cub, who had momentarily left her little one to search for game. Cuoi threw the cub to the ground and scrambled in terror up into the sheltering branches of the nearest tree. A moment later the tigress came crashing through the underbrush and growled ferociously as she saw the motionless body of her dead offspring; for Cuoi, in his haste to escape, had thrown the cub to the ground with such force it had been killed.

Up in the tree, Cuoi held his breath, for he knew that he could expect the worst. But then a strange thing happened. The tigress walked to a nearby stream and gathered the leaves from a certain banyan tree. She chewed them into a pulp which she then applied to the head of the dead cub. Immediately the young tiger jumped to its feet and ran about as if nothing had happened.

When the tigress and her cub had disappeared, Cuoi let himself down from his refuge and made his way to the miraculous banyan tree. He gathered a handful of leaves and took them with him. On the way home he came upon a dead dog lying by the side of the road. Cuoi then chewed the leaves into a pulp, as he had seen the tigress do, and applied them to the dog's head. After a few minutes the animal was restored to life; it jumped to its feet and bounded away. Cuoi realized that the leaves of the banyan tree had the miraculous power to restore the dead to life. So he uprooted the tree, dragged it home, and replanted it in the middle of his yard. He also warned his mother never to throw refuse or dirty water where the tree was planted.

"Otherwise," he said jokingly, "the tree will fly away to the sky."

Cuoi's mother paid no attention to this admonition and continued to throw rubbish at the very spot where

her son had requested her not to. One day the tree began to slowly pull itself from the soil and to fly up
into the sky.

Somehow Cuoi's joke was coming true!

Returning from his chores, Cuoi saw the tree floating
away and ran after it in great haste and grasped its
roots. But his slight weight was not sufficient to bring
the tree down to earth again. Instead, he was carried
with it into the sky.

After many days of travel Cuoi and the tree reached
a strange new world where there was a permanent
calm. It was the Moon. Cuoi planted the tree there and
sat down to figure a way out of his terrible predicament;
but there was no solution. There on the Moon he has
sat waiting, year in and year out, even until today.

The children of Vietnam say that on certain nights,
in the curve of the moon, they can see the lone image
of Cuoi seated at the foot of a banyan tree. They maintain that sometimes he even turns his head to look at
them and smile. They then wave to him and sing:

> *"Cuoi, Cuoi, the dream-time boy,*
> *Alone, alone, on the Moon;*
> *Playing with the stars in the lost twilight*
> *Until late has become soon."*

THE BUFFALO BOY AND THE BANYAN TREE

5

THE GAMBLER'S
WIFE

ONCE THERE lived a man named Trong Qui
who was so fond of gambling that he squandered all his money on games of chance. Trong
Qui came from an illustrious family, and his father,
Phung Lap Ngon, was a mandarin greatly admired
for his integrity and righteousness.

Trong Qui's wife, Tu Nhi Khanh, was sweet-
tempered, virtuous, and beautiful beyond description.
Her father had given her in marriage to the son of
his friend, Phung Lap Ngon.

From early childhood, Tu Nhi Khanh had dreamed
of marrying a gifted scholar, a holder of many degrees.
But instead, it was her misfortune to be married to a
gambler and wastrel.

Tu Nhi Khanh tried to dissuade her husband from

his dangerous passion, but her pleas availed nothing. Trong Qui was discharged from his job for debts and intoxication, and chose as companions a group of rascals who cheated and robbed him at every opportunity. He cared neither for his parents nor for his wife and children. He lived merrily, frequented teahouses, and wasted his time and money. People began to call him the "King of Gambling." Finally, Tu Nhi Khanh became silent and resigned herself to fate.

One day Trong Qui met a rich merchant named Do Tam, who was also an inveterate gambler. Do Tam was actually attracted by the great beauty of Tu Nhi Khanh and secretly determined that he would win her away from her husband.

For his part, Trong Qui coveted Do Tam's wealth, but he was not as clever as the latter at cards. Do Tam permitted Trong Qui to win various sums of money from him over a period of weeks, and then one day placed a large sum of money on the table and said:

"Dear friend, you have been very lucky for the past weeks. Today, let us play for some really big stakes. You cannot cover this sum, I know; but let us play for it anyhow. If you win, you keep it; if I win, I will take your wife as your bond."

Trong Qui was slightly intoxicated, but looked at the money with covetous eyes and thought;

"Why not? I have been lucky lately and I may win again. If it comes to the worst, I can work hard to redeem my wife." And he accepted the bet.

THE GAMBLER'S WIFE

In three hands Trong Qui had lost everything, and could do nothing but ask Tu Nhi Khanh to come to Do Tam's home. He said to her: "I have been mad, but it is too late now to make amends. I have staked my happiness and lost. You must remain here with Do Tam until I can earn the money to repay the debt and take you home again."

Tu Nhi Khanh was sick with horror, for she knew that she would not be able to resist the advances of the rich merchant. Her face turned pale, but she tried to hide her emotions and said to Do Tam in a meek voice:

"When one must choose between poverty and wealth, there is a clear choice. This meeting should have a happy ending. If you deign to accept me into your house, I will be your servant as I have been the servant of my husband. But first I would like to return home to say farewell to my children.

Do Tam was delighted to hear this speech, for he had expected some resistance on the part of Tu Nhi Khan, and he was only too happy to grant her request.

The betrayed woman returned home, took her two young children into her arms, covered them with kisses, and said:

"My little ones, I must abandon you, but it will not be to live with another man, whatever may be the wrongs of your father." Then she committed suicide.

This act brought Trong Qui to his senses, and his grief was profound and sincere. A real change took place in his character. He foreswore gambling and was truly ashamed of his former life. Unfortunately his meager means diminished day by day, and he soon became entirely destitute.

Having learned that one of his old friends was mandarin in Qui Hoa, he decided to go there to beg for help. At the halfway point of the journey, he became exhausted and sat down to rest at the foot of a tree. Suddenly he heard a voice from above.

"Is it you, Trong Qui? If you remember old associations, wait for me in the temple of Truong Vuong on the tenth day of the coming month. Do not fail to be there, and do not believe that the world of the dead is without communication with that of the living."

Trong Qui recognized his wife's voice. He raised his eyes towards the sky and saw a black cloud, which passed fleetingly towards the north. He thought himself the victim of an illusion.

Nevertheless, on the tenth day of the following month he went to the temple of Truong Vuong as directed. When he arrived there, it was already late. The evening shadows had enveloped the melancholy landscape in silence. Trong Qui entered the temple, and stretched out in the gallery reserved for pilgrims.

Towards the end of the third watch, he heard the sound of gentle weeping. Distant at first, the sound drew nearer. Trong Qui then made out the figure of Tu Nhi Khanh in the darkness.

"After my death," said his wife, "the Emperor of Jade took pity on me and permitted me to enter his service. Until the present time I have been too busy to see you again. It was in the course of a mission that I met you yesterday; I was going to carry rain to the lands of the North. But for this fortuitous circumstance, we would not have found each other again."

Trong Qui expressed his regrets for his misdeeds and begged her to pardon him. The two lovers talked until dawn. Before leaving him, Tu Nhi Khanh said:

"I have had the opportunity of attending the audiences of the Emperor of Jade, and I have heard the fairies announce that the prosperity of the Ho is approaching an end. During the year of Binh Ti, war will break out and 200,000 men will perish. All those who have failed to cultivate the tree of virtue will be delivered to torment. Order and Peace will be reestablished by a Righteous One of the Le family. I beg you to rear our sons properly and, when the moment comes, advise them to follow this hero without fear or hesitation."

Then she vanished.

Trong Qui did all that Tu Nhi Khanh had requested. He devoted his life to the care and education of their sons and never remarried. When the future Le Thai To rebelled in the region of Lam Son, the two sons of Trong Qui recruited partisans in his behalf. After the accession of the Great King, both rose to the rank of privy councilor and, even in our day, their progeny prosper in the district of Khoai.

6

THE TAILOR
AND THE
MANDARIN

IN THE capital of Vietnam there was once a certain tailor who was renowned for his skill. Every garment that left his shop had to fit the client perfectly, regardless of the latter's weight, build, age, or bearing.

One day a high mandarin sent for the tailor and ordered a ceremonial robe.

After taking the necessary measurements, the tailor respectfully asked the mandarin how long he had been in the service.

"What does that have to do with the cut of my robe?" asked the mandarin good-naturedly.

"It is of great importance, sire," responded the tailor. "You know that a newly appointed mandarin, impressed with his own importance, carries his head high and his chest out. We must take this into consideration and cut the rear lappet shorter than the front.

"Later, little by little we lengthen the rear lappet and shorten the front one; the lappets are cut exactly the same length when the mandarin reaches the half-way point of his career.

"Finally, when bent over with the fatigue of long years of service and the burden of age, he aspires only to join his ancestors in heaven, the robe must be made longer in the back than in the front.

"Thus you see, sire, that a tailor who does not know the seniority of the mandarins cannot fit them correctly."

7

THE ORIGIN OF BANH GIAY AND BANH CHUNG

BANH GIAY and Banh Chung are two types of delicacies which are very popular with the Vietnamese people.

Banh Giay is served regularly at festivals and ceremonies. It is a rounded, convex cake of glutinous or *nep* rice, which resembles white dough, soft and sticky. Its cupola-shaped top is said to resemble the shape of the heavenly vault.

Banh Chung is served particularly at the Vietnamese New Year's festival, which occurs during the first three days of the first month of the lunar calendar. It is a square cake, wrapped in banana leaves and tied with lacings of flexible bamboo slivers. It is a very rich food for the interior contains a filling of bean paste to which may be added small bits of pork meat, both fat and lean. This filling, which is amply seasoned, is pressed between layers of glutinous *nep* rice. Its square shape is considered a symbol of the thankfulness of the Vietnamese people for the great abundance of the Earth, which has supplied them with nutritious food throughout the four seasons of the year.

Here is the story about the origin of Banh Giay and Banh Chung.

*　　*　　*

King Hung-Vuong the Sixth had already lived a long and useful life. When he had finally repelled the An invaders and restored peace to his kingdom, he determined to relinquish the throne, with all its worldly responsibilities, in order to enjoy mental repose during his declining years.

The king was the father of twenty-two sons, all worthy princes. From among them he had to choose an heir and successor. It was a difficult task and the king was not certain how to determined the qualities of a future sovereign in his sons. He thought about it for a long time and finally arrived at a novel solution. Since there is much to be learned from travel, he decided to send his sons on a journey.

He called the twenty-two princes together and said "Go forth, all of you, to the farthest corners of the earth and search out for me recipes and foodstuffs that I have not yet tasted, but which I would greatly enjoy. He who returns with the best dish will rule this kingdom."

The princes dispersed and made their preparations. Twenty-one of them set out on distant journeys to search for the dish that would most please the king. Some went north into cold and inhospitable areas, and others journeyed south, east and west.

But there was one prince who did not leave the royal palace. He was sixteenth in rank and his name was Lang Lieu. His mother had died while he was still very young, and unlike his brothers he had never known the warmth of maternal love. He had only his old nurse to look after him.

Prince Lang Lieu was at a complete loss and had no idea about how he might set about procuring a new dish for the king. There was no one to advise him, so he remained in the palace, lost in gloomy meditation.

One night a genie appeared to the prince in a dream and said: "Prince, I know of your youthful loneliness and understand your anxieties. I have been sent here to help you, so that you will be able to please your royal father. Therefore, do not despair. It is a law of nature that man cannot live without rice; it is man's chief food. For that reason, you will first take a quantity of glutinous rice, some beans, some fat and lean pork meat, and spices. Pluck some banana leaves and from split bamboo cut flexible lacings. All these materials symbolize the abundance of the Earth.

"Soak the rice in clean water and boil part of it. When it is well-cooked, pound it into a cupola-shaped, plain cake.

"Now prepare a stuffing of bean paste and bits of pork. Place this between layers of rice. Wrap the whole

THE ORIGIN OF BANH GIAY AND BANH CHUNG

in banana leaves and press it into a square shape. Then bind it with the flexible bamboo lacings. Cook it for a day and the cake will be ready for eating."

Then the genie disappeared and the prince awakened to find himself lying in bed, looking at the ceiling with wide-open eyes and repeating the words that he had heard. Could he have been dreaming? In the morning he revealed the secret to his old nurse and together they collected the proper materials and prepared the cakes as directed.

After the apricot trees had blossomed once, the twenty-one princes returned from their quests. They were weary from their long travels but happy with anticipation. Each prepared his dish with his own hands, using the special foods and materials that he had brought back with him. Each seemed confident that his dish would win the prize.

On the appointed day the dishes were brought before the king. Twenty-one times the king tasted, and twenty-one times he shook his head in disapproval. Then Prince Lang Leiu modestly presented his two cakes—one, white and "round as the sky" and the other, steaming hot and "square as the earth," wrapped in banana leaves with flexible bamboo lacings. The prince untied the leaves and displayed a soft, sticky, green cake, which he cut with the bamboo. The inside was white and lemon-yellow and studded with opaline bits of fat and brown bits of lean pork meat.

The king accepted a piece of the square cake and tasted it. Then he picked up a second piece, and then a third, until he had eaten the cake completely. Then he ate the round cake also.

"Is there any more." he asked, smacking his lips, his eyes dancing with pleasure.

"How did you make them?" he asked in wonder.

Prince Lang Lieu told the story of how the genie had appeared to him and had instructed him in the selection of foodstuffs and the manner of making the cakes. The Court listened in silence.

The king was greatly impressed with the revelation for it attested divine support. He surmised that in the handling of state affairs, divine inspiration would not be lacking for the young prince. He accordingly named Lang Lieu the winner and appointed him his heir and successor. He decided that the round loaf should be called Banh Giay and the square one, Bang Chung, and ordered his ministers to give the recipes to the Vietnamese people.

8

A LIE
AND A HALF

RETURNING TO his native village after a distant journey, a certain traveller told the following tale: "During my travels I saw a great ship, the very length of which defied the imagination. A young boy of twelve left the bow of this ship to walk to the stern. By the time he arrived at the mast, his hair and his beard had already turned white, and he died of old age before he could reach the stern."

A native of the village, who had heard tales of this nature before, then spoke up: "I see nothing so remarkable in what you have just related. I myself once passed through a forest filled with trees so tall that it was impossible to estimate their height. In fact, a bird which tried to reach their tops flew for ten years without even approaching the halfway mark."

"That's an abominable lie!" shouted the first story-teller. "How could such a thing be possible?"

"How?" asked the other quietly. "Why, if it is not the truth, where would a tree be found that could be the mast for the ship that you have just described?"

9

THE LAND
OF BLISS

IN VIETNAM, when a man sees a really beautiful woman, he may remark to his neighbor: "Look at that wonderful beauty. Perhaps she comes from the Land of Bliss." He is referring of course to a story told long ago by Tu Thuc, who once had the good fortune to visit this fairyland. Here is the tale.

*   *   *

Over five centuries ago, during the reign of King Tran Thuan Tong, there lived a young mandarin named Tu Thuc, who was chief of the Tien Du district. He was a very learned man and possessed many precious books. In these he could find all the knowledge of the world except the location of the Land of Bliss, and this was what he longed to know.

As a small boy Tu Thuc had been told that the Chinese Emperor Duong Minh Hoang had by chance discovered the Land of Bliss one night when the August moon was full. There he had found women with wonderful peach-blossom complexions wearing rainbow-colored dresses with long, flaring sleeves. It was land of eternal youth and pleasure, and one's time was spent in laughter, music, and dancing. The emperor learned the wonderful "Khuc Nghe Thuong" dance from the fairies themselves. On his return to earth he taught this dance to the ladies of the imperial palace, who would then dance for him in the silver moonlight as he sipped his perfumed wine.

From his boyhood Tu Thuc had dreamed of the Land of Bliss, and his greatest ambition was to visit this remarkable land.

One day Tu Thuc passed an old pagoda which was renowned for its glorious peonies. It was during the Flower Festival of the year Binh Ti, and the red peonies were in full bloom. It happened that a young maiden of radiant beauty and sweet countenance had lowered a branch to admire the blossoms, and as she did so it broke off in her hand. The priests of the pagoda arrested her and imposed a fine, which she was unable to pay. Tu Thuc had observed these proceedings, and although he had insufficient money to pay the fine, he generously offered his brocade coat in exchange for the maiden's freedom. This offer was accepted and Tu Thuc was praised by everyone in the district when his kind gesture became known.

Some years later, tired of the "circle of honors and worldly interests," Tu Thuc resigned his office in order to be able to visit the "blue mountains and emerald-green waters." He retired to Tong-Son, a place of many beautiful springs and splendid grottoes.

One day, taking his lute, a book of poems, and a gourd of wine, he set out to wander through the great forest, where graceful boughs wove canopies from tree to tree. He crossed many streams and visited the famous Pink Mountain, the Cave of the Green Clouds, and the Lai River. As he walked he composed verses in praise of nature's wild and magic charm.

One day he awoke early in the morning and beheld five pastel clouds which shimmered and glittered above the sea, as they unfolded into the form of lotus flowers. Enticed by this vision, he rowed towards the clouds and saw a magic mountain floating on the sea. He stepped ashore, and deeply moved by the beauty of the scenery about him, composed this verse:

A thousand reflections quiver in these lofty boughs;
The flowers of the grotto greet the arriving guest.
Near the spring, where then is the herb gatherer?
A lone boatman rows on the stream,
And his guitar sounds two notes.
The boat glides lazily, the gourd offers its wine.
Shall we ask the boatman of Vo Lang:
"Where are the peach trees of the Land of Bliss?"

Having completed the poem, Tu Thuc saw the sides of the mountain suddenly open and from the interior there came a strange, rustling sound. Was it an invitation to enter?

He entered the dark cavern and felt the mountain

close behind him. For some distance the cavern was so narrow that he was forced to crawl on his hands and knees, but then it became lofty and wide. As he approached its deepest point, a golden light greeted him. Looking up, he saw that the rocks above were as clear as the white clouds of the purest sky. Grasping the jagged edges of the rocks, he began to climb.

Near the summit the air was perfumed with the scent of lilies and roses. A crystalline spring flowed at his feet, and he saw gold and silver fish swimming in its waters. The broad lotus leaves floating on the surface glistened with all the colors of the rainbow, appearing as brilliant lights. A bridge of marble led over the stream to a wonderful garden, where hidden fairies sang songs so soft and harmonious that no human voice could hope to match them.

The path, strewn with fallen petals, led to a garden with boughs shimmering with starry flowers. Wonderful birds mingled with the flowers and poured forth their melodious songs. A flock of peacocks, tail-feathers spread, stood on the green grass which was covered with iridescent petals. And all around more petals kept falling like flakes of snow. Tu Thuc felt lost in another world. But suddenly the murmur of voices returned him to reality.

From behind a lacquered gate a group of lovely maidens, dressed in blue, and with sparkling stars in their hair, came forth to meet him.

"Greetings to our handsome bridegroom," said one of them, and then they all disappeared into the palace to announce his arrival. A short while later they returned and, bowing, implored him to enter.

Tu Thuc followed the maidens into a magnificent hall with brocaded walls and heavily gilded doors. A soft and gentle melody floated in the air, and harps sounded sweetly at his approach.

A majestic lady in a snow-white silken dress was seated on a richly carved throne. She motioned him to a graceful sandalwood chair and then asked:

"Learned scholar and lover of beautiful sites, do you know what land this is?"

"It is true that I have visited many blue mountains and great forests," he answered politely, "but truly I had never hoped to see such a wonderful land. Would the Most Noble Lady tell me where I find myself?"

The lady smiled and said:

"How could a man from the world of brown dust recognize this land? You are in the sixth of the thirty-six grottoes of Phi Lai Mountain, which floats on the wide ocean and appears and vanishes according to the winds. I am the Fairy Queen of the Nam Nhac summit and my name is Nguy. I know that you have a beautiful soul and a noble heart, and I welcome you."

Then the Fairy Queen motioned to the maidens, and they ushered in a beautiful and modest young girl who had not been with them before. Tu Thuc at once recognized the young maiden he had befriended at the pagoda.

The Fairy Queen spoke again:

"This is my daughter, Giang Huong. The day she was in distress you were the only one who offered to help her. We have never forgotten your noble and generous gesture, and now I am able to show my gratitude. I offer you her hand in marriage, and henceforth my daughter's life will be bound to yours."

The wedding was celebrated that very day, and all the fairies from the grottoes were invited. A great feast was prepared, and the nupitals were performed with great pomp.

Then followed many pleasant days of laughter and happiness in the Land of Bliss. The weather was neither hot nor cold, for it was a land of eternal spring. The boughs in the garden were laden with flowers more beautiful than the rose, and it seemed that there was nothing more that Tu Thuc could wish for.

Still, as time passed, he began to feel nostalgia for his native village. He would often remain alone at night on the beach and gaze into the distance.

One day, looking towards the south, he saw a boat gliding on the sea. Pointing, he said to Giang Huong: "It is likely that that boat is going in the direction from which I came. I cannot hide my feelings any longer; I think constantly of my home there. Would you understand if I were to return for a while?"

Giang Huong hesitated at the idea of parting, but Tu Thuc insisted: "It is only a matter of a few weeks. Once I have seen my relatives, I promise to return."

The Fairy Queen was consulted and said: "If he

wishes to return to the world of toil and sadness, what is the good of keeping him here? His heart is still laden with earthly memories, and his wish shall be granted."

Tu Thuc was then asked to close his eyes for a moment, and when he opened them he was back on earth.

He asked the way to his village and was told that he was already there. Yet he failed to recognize the surroundings. Instead of old friends and acquaintances, he met people he had never seen before. He inquired of the old men in the square and told them his name. None of them knew it. He left the village, convinced that it was not his own. As he was leaving he met a very old man.

"Excuse me, venerable grandfather," he said to the old man, "my name is Tu Thuc, and I am looking for my native village. Would you be kind enough to show me the way?"

"Tu Thuc? Tu Thuc?" repeated the old man as he searched his mind. "When I was a boy I was told that one of my ancestors named Tu Thuc had been chief of the Tien Du district. But he resigned his office over a hundred years ago and set off for an unknown destination and never returned. Many people said that he was borne to Heaven, but more likely he was lost in some ravine. That was near the end of the Tran dynasty, and we are now under the fourth Le king."

Tu Thuc then gave an account of his miraculous experience, and realized he had stayed in the Land of Bliss for exactly one hundred years.

"I have heard that a year on Earth is only a day in

the Land of Bliss. So you are my most venerable ancestor, Tu Thuc," continued the old man, "please let me show you your old home."

And he led Tu Thuc to a deserted place, where there was nothing to be seen except a dilapidated hut, entirely beyond repair.

Tu Thuc was unhappy and disappointed. He longed to return to the Land of Bliss as rapidly as possible. All the people that he had once known on Earth had been dead for many years, and the ways and manners of the younger generations completely bewildered him.

So he set out again in the direction of the Yellow Mountains in search of the fairyland, and disappeared. But whether he found the Land of Bliss or became lost in the mountains, no one knows.

10

THE MOSQUITO

IN VIETNAM the mosquitoes are troublesome and even unbearable at certain times of the year. Everyone detests them, but very few know their history and the reasons why these cursed insects buzz unceasingly in our ears and attempt to suck our blood. This legend will explain their origin.

*   *   *

Ngoc Tam, a modest farmer, had married Nhan Diep. The two young people were poor but in excellent health, and they seemed destined to enjoy the happiness of a simple rural life. The husband worked in the paddy and cultivated a small field of mulberry trees, and the wife engaged in raising silkworms.

But Nhan Diep was a coquette at heart. She was lazy, and dreamed of luxury and pleasures. She was also clever enough to hide her desires and ambitions from her husband, whose love was genuine, but neither demanding nor discerning. He supposed his wife to be content with her lot and happy in her daily chores.

Ngoc Tam toiled diligently, hoping to ease their poverty and improve their station in life.

Suddenly Nhan Diep was carried away by death. Ngoc Tam was plunged into such deep sorrow that he would not leave his wife's body and opposed its burial.

One day, after having sold his possessions, he embarqued in a sampan with the coffin and sailed away.

One morning he found himself at the foot of a fragrant, green hill which perfumed the countryside.

He went ashore and discovered a thousand rare flowers and orchards of trees laden with the most varied kinds of fruit.

There he met an old man who supported himself with a bamboo cane. His hair was white as cotton and his face wrinkled and sunburned, but under his blond eyelashes his eyes sparkled like those of a young boy. By this last trait Ngoc Tam recognized the genie of medicine, who traveled throughout the world on his mountain, Thien Thai, to teach his science to the men of the earth and to alleviate their ills.

Ngoc Tam threw himself at the genie's feet.

Then the genie spoke to him:

"Having learned of your virtues, Ngoc Tam, I have stopped my mountain on your route. If you wish, I will admit you to the company of my disciples."

Ngoc Tam thanked him profusely but said that he desired only to live with his wife. He had never thought

THE MOSQUITO

of any life other than the one he would lead with her, and he begged the genie to bring her back to life.

The genie looked at him with kindness mixed with pity and said:

"Why do you cling to this world of bitterness and gall? The rare joys of this life are only a snare. How foolish you were to entrust your destiny to a weak and inconstant being! I want to grant your wishes, but I fear that you will regret it later."

Then, on the genie's order, Ngoc Tam opened the coffin; he cut the tip of his finger and let three drops of blood fall on Nhan Diep's body. The latter opened her eyes slowly, as if awakening from a deep sleep. Then her faculties quickly returned.

"Do not forget your obligations," the genie said to her. "Remember your husband's devotion. May you both be happy."

On the voyage home Ngoc Tam rowed day and night, eager to reach his native land again. One evening he went ashore in a certain port to buy provisions.

During his absence a large ship came alongside the wharf, and the owner, a rich merchant, was struck by Nhan Diep's beauty. He entered into conversation with her and invited her to have refreshments aboard his vessel. As soon as she was aboard, he gave the order to cast off and sailed away.

Ngoc Tam searched an entire month for his wife before locating her aboard the merchant's vessel.

She answered his questions without the least hesitation, but had grown accustomed to her new life. It satisfied her completely and she refused to return home with him. Then for the first time, Ngoc Tam saw her in her true light. Suddenly he felt all love for her vanish, and he no longer desired her return.

"You are free," he said to her. "Only return to me the three drops of blood that I gave to bring you back to life. I do not want to leave the least trace of myself in you."

Happy to be set free so cheaply, Nhan Diep took a knife and cut the tip of her finger. But, as soon as the blood began to flow, she turned pale and sank to the ground. An instant later she was dead.

*   *   *

Even so, the light-hearted frivolous woman could not resign herself to leave this world forever. She returned in the form of a small insect and followed Ngoc Tam relentlessly, in order to steal the three drops of blood from him, which would restore her to human life. Day and night she worried her former husband, buzzing around him incessantly, protesting her innocence, and begging his pardon. Later, she received the name of "mosquito." Unfortunately for us, her race has multiplied many times.

11

THE FAIRY'S PORTRAIT

IN THE early years of the Le dynasty, there lived in the village of Bich Cau a young scholar named Tu Uyen. He was known far and wide, for he came from a distinguished family of scholars and was reared in the literary tradition. He spent his days and nights in study, and in reciting aloud his favorite poems, intoning the words with great pleasure.

There were many fair and rich young maidens in the province who would have liked to marry Tu Uyen, but he wished to marry no one.

One day, in the middle of the Spring Festival, Tu Uyen decided to go into the open fields to enjoy the spring air and the warm sun.

It was very beautiful in the countryside; nature was luxuriant and wonderful. The rice fields were green, trees were swaying in the gentle air, and wild flowers peeped out from the verdant meadows.

Tu Uyen turned his face towards the sun, looked into the sky, and listened to the birds singing.

"How lovely it is when spring comes," he thought. "The sun warms me, and the gentle breeze plays over me. O how I am blessed! If only this could last forever!"

At last evening approached, and Tu Uyen turned back, retracing his steps homeward. As he passed the ornate Tien Tich pagoda, he raised his eyes and saw a maiden of surprising beauty standing near a blossoming peach tree. From her delicate figure, her beautiful dress, and her noble bearing, it was evident that she was no ordinary woman. As the moonlight played on her pale face and glistening eyes, she looked dreamy and ethereal.

Fascinated by the maiden's appearance, Tu Uyen grew bold, bowed to her politely, and said:

"Most honored lady, as night is drawing near, may your humble servant, this unworthy scholar of Bich Cau village, accompany you to your abode."

The beautiful maiden curtsied and in a graceful and courteous manner, thanked the young man for his consideration, and said she would be delighted to have him accompany her. Then they walked side by side, emulating each other in composing love songs and poems.

But when they reached the Quang Minh temple, the lady suddenly vanished. It was only then that Tu

Uyen realized that he had met a fairy. He remained there for some time in a trance, unable to tear himself away.

When Tu Uyen reached home, he continued to think of the beautiful fairy. He supposed that she was now dwelling far away, above mountains and trees. He spoke to no one of the strange encounter, for he had fallen deeply in love. In the days that followed, he lay dreaming of her, unable to sleep during the five watches of the night and unable to eat during the six divisions of the day. He was struck with the languor of love, that mysterious illness for which there is no cure.

Silently he prayed to the gods that he might die soon, so he would be with the beautiful fairy in another world, for he was convinced that their destinies were entwined. One night a bearded old man appeared to him in a dream and told him to go to the Eastern bridge of the River To Lich, where he would find the maiden he loved.

Tu Uyen awakened and, unable to constrain his joy, ran to the Eastern bridge as dawn was breaking.

He waited for a long time but no one came. He was about to leave when he saw an old man selling pictures. Tu Uyen looked at them and discovered the portrait of a woman who looked exactly like the one he had met under the peach tree.

He bought the portrait, took it home, and hung it on the wall of his study. His heart warmed as he lovingly gazed at the picture. Then he stroked and caressed it, whispering ardent phrases of love and devotion.

During the day, he would stop his reading, put aside his books, and admire the picture. He would get up in the middle of the night, light a candle, take up the picture, and kiss it as if it were real.

At each meal he would place two bowls and two pairs of chopsticks on the table. He would not serve himself until the lady of the portrait had been served, acting as a husband would towards his wife.

One day, when he was admiring the portrait, the maiden opened her eyes, and smiled. Taken aback, Tu Uyen rubbed his eyes and stared at her. Then she grew taller and taller and stepped forth from the picture, bowing deeply.

Without raising her eyes, she spoke in a soft, musical voice and said: "Here I am, my lord. You have waited long enough for me."

"Who are you, most honored lady?" asked Tu Uyen.

"My name is Giang Kieu and I am a fairy," she replied. "Perhaps you remember our first meeting under a blossoming peach tree during the Spring Festival. There is a great source of predestined happiness in your family, and this made possible our first meeting. Your love and faith in me have moved the Fairy Queen to send me down here to be your wife."

The young scholar's dream was truly fulfilled, and he was transported into a new world of untold happiness and delight. His house was transformed into a heaven by Giang Kieu's sweet presence and the magic of her love.

THE FAIRY'S PORTRAIT

Tu Yyen loved her dearly and followed her everywhere, forgetting his books and neglecting his studies.

When Giang Kieu reproached him for this, he looked deep into her eyes and said:

"My beloved Giang Kieu, I was once sad and lonely. Then you came into my life and changed everything. You become more beautiful everyday, and it is only natural that I crave to be near you. I cannot act otherwise."

"If you want a successful career, you must listen to me," replied the fairy. "Do not idle any longer; begin your studies anew, or I shall leave you."

He obeyed her reluctantly, but his mind was distracted. Finally he took to wine. One day, when he was drunk, the fairy returned to the picture. He regretted his weakness and prayed for her to come back again.

"Beautiful Giang Kieu," he implored, "this one is your slave and begs forgiveness. What will I do without your beloved presence and sweet love?"

Although the fairy did not stir from the picture, Tu Uyen refused to give up. Day after day he waited for her to return, clinging desperately to fading hopes. Again and again he talked to the lady in the picture, promising to obey her; he even talked of committing suicide. At last Giang Kieu stepped out of the picture.

"My lord, if you do not listen to me this time," she said, "I shall be forced to leave you forever."

Tu Uyen gave her his solemn promise and vowed that he would never again disobey her. Fearful of losing her, he began to study hard and soon passed his examinations, qualifying as a mandarin.

Then a son was born to Tu Uyen and Giang Kieu, and a nurse was hired to take care of him.

One day, when the boy was just over a year old, the air suddenly grew balmy, the sun shone brighter than ever, and celestial music was heard from afar.

Giang Kieu became serious and said to her husband:

"My lord, I have lived with you for more than two years. My time on earth is up, and it pleases the Fairy Queen to call me back to the Purple Hills. Please, do not look depressed and alarmed. Your name is also on the list of the Immortals; let us go to Heaven together."

She then turned to the nurse and said: "Our earthly riches are yours now. Please rear our son properly. When he has passed all his examinations, we will come back to take him to our abode in Heaven."

Giang Kieu burned incense, murmured prayers, and then two miraculous swans, with golden wreaths around their necks and twinkling stars on their heads, appeared before them.

They climbed onto the backs of the swans and flew away into the warm, blue sky. Sweet celestial music filled the air, as if the gods rejoiced to receive them in Heaven. Seeing this, the villagers built a temple at Tu Uyen's house, in which to worship the Immortal.

* * *

The Tu Uyen temple still stands at the same location in Hanoi; the Eastern Bridge (located between Sugar

Street and Copper Street according to legend) and the
River To Lich, have both disappeared with time.

12

THE BETEL
AND THE
ARECA TREE

(This legend is one of the oldest and best known in Vietnam)

URING THE reign of the fourth (some say
the third) King Hung Vuong, there lived a
mandarin named Cao, who had two sons,
Tan and Lang. Although not twins, they resembled
each other like two drops of water, so much so their
mother could not tell them apart. They had the same
lofty brows, the same straight noses, and the same intelligent, sparkling eyes. They were both handsome,
they loved each other tenderly, and one was never seen
without the other.

The two brothers were still young when a fire
burned down their home, causing the death of their
parents and the loss of all their possessions. The two
young men were left in want, and to avoid charity, went
out into the world in search of work.

By chance they knocked at the door of Mandarin

Luu, a very pious man, who had been an intimate friend of their parents. He received them into his stately mansion with a most cordial welcome. He had no sons of his own, but had a daughter, as fair as a white lotus, and as fresh as a spring rose.

Wishing to tighten their bonds of friendship and affection, Mandarin Luu offered to give his daughter in marriage to one of the young men. They were both attracted by the good looks and graceful manners of the pretty maiden, and each secretly loved her.

Their hearts were equally generous, however, and each insisted that the other should marry the girl. For her part, the maiden was unable to choose between the two young men, they were so alike.

Tan and Lang would never have come to an agreement had the mandarin not used a clever little trick to find out which was the elder. He ordered a special meal prepared for his daughter and the brothers. Two bowls of rice were brought to the table, but only one pair of chopsticks. Without hesitation, Lang picked up the chopsticks and in a very respectful manner handed them to Tan. Tan accepted them naturally, and Mandarin Luu immediately chose the elder brother to be the husband of his daughter.

*   *   *

Tan was now the happiest man on earth. He loved his bride passionately, and they pledged eternal love for each other. He had never known such happiness and spent his time composing love poems to describe his bliss and to show his deep affection. He completely neglected his brother, who seemed to have left his thoughts forever.

After his brother's wedding, Lang triumphed easily over his secret love for the young woman. He gladly accepted his lot, for he wanted only the happiness of his beloved elder brother. But gradually he realized that Tan had become indifferent and cold towards him.

Lang waited for a long time in silence for a sign of friendship and love, but it did not come. Poor Lang!

One morning he said to himself:

"Alas! My elder brother no longer loves me. Why should I stay here at all, unloved and unwanted? The sooner I leave this place the better."

He sprang to his feet and left the house, for he could no longer bear his grief. For a long time he walked, insensible to fatigue, until he reached the dark, blue sea. A cold wind was blowing, the sun had sunk below the horizon, and the last gleams of the sunset were swallowed up by the immense body of water.

Completely exhausted, hungry and thirsty, Lang sat down on the grass by the edge of the sea and wept until he died of grief, and was changed into a white, chalky rock.

* * *

When Tan learned that Lang had stolen away from the house, he was extremely sorry and ashamed of his selfishness. Full of regret and troubled by his conscience, he set out to look for his young brother.

He traversed the same route, crossed the same hills, and passed through the same forests, until he too

THE BETEL AND THE ARECA TREE

reached the dark, blue sea. Exhausted, he sat down with his back against a white chalky rock, and wept until he died, changing into a tree with a straight trunk and green palm leaves. Tan had become the areca tree.

When the young bride found that her husband had left their home, she missed him so much that she set off in search. She traversed the very same route, and arrived at the site of the white chalky rock and the areca tree. Entirely worn out, she lay down to rest at the foot of the tree. Tears of despair rolled down her cheeks, and she kept on crying sorrowfully and thinking of her husband until she died. She was turned into the creeping betel plant, which twined itself around the stately trunk of the areca tree.

Enlightened by a dream, the peasants of the vicinity built a temple, in commemoration of the fraternal and conjugal love of the unfortunate brothers and the maiden. On the facade of the temple they inscribed the following motto: "Brothers united, spouses faithful."

*   *   *

Years later, during a period of exceptional drought which marked the end of the reign of the fourth King Hung Vuong, the areca tree and the creeping betel plant were the only green things remaining amidst the desolation. At the news of this miracle, pilgrims from all parts of the kingdom journeyed to the temple.

King Hung Vuong himself went there, and learned the story from the village notables. He was impressed by the tale and attempted to learn the divine intentions by asking his counselors the meaning of it all, but no one knew the answer.

Finally, the minister of justice, a great and wise old man, said to the king:

"Sire, when one wishes to assure himself of the consanguinity of brothers and sisters, or when one wishes to know the paternity of a child, the persons concerned are bled, and their blood is collected in the same bowl. If the blood coagulates the response is positive. We could crush together some leaves of the betel plant, with the fruit of the tree, and a fragment of rock."

This advice was followed. The rock was heated and reduced to powder and the mixture took on a beautiful red color; the proof was clear.

The king meditated and said: "This is the true symbol of fraternal and conjugal love. Let the tree and the plant be grown everywhere in commemoration of this beautiful story."

Brothers and sisters began to chew the quid of betel to demonstrate fraternal love, and newly wedded couples chew it to demonstrate conjugal love. The habit spread very quickly, until in the end it became the custom to offer the quid of betel at all social meetings "to maintain mutual affection."

THE BETEL AND THE ARECA TREE

13

TWO BOXES
OF TEA

D O NOT smile with disbelief: there are some
honest mandarins. There are even those who
practice honesty with a certain delicacy. Listen
to the following true account.

Trinh Dam Toan was a mandarin who refused all
gifts, no matter of what nature. One day a merchant
for whom he had done many favors timidly begged
him to accept two boxes of tea. The gift was modest
and ritual.

The mandarin at first refused. But the merchant,
who did not dare to insist other than by a respectful
silence, maintained such a sincere attitude that Trinh
Dam Toan departed from his principles, in order not
to offend the man.

When the latter had left, the mandarin observed
that the two boxes of tea were quite heavy.

When opened, they were found to be filled with gold.

What should the mandarin do now? He closed the boxes, sent for the merchant, and said:

"I accepted your gift because I thought that we were out of tea in the house, but I was wrong, we have more tea than we can use. Therefore, although I appreciate your thoughtfulness, I must return your present."

TWO BOXES OF TEA

14

DA TRANG'S CRABS

VERY morning from early dawn, Da Trang the hunter would leave his straw-thatched hut, and plunge into the forest with his bow and arrows. He would return late at night, bringing the game that he had killed during the day.

One day he happened to pass a shrine where two black serpents with white spots were lying in the sun. At first he was afraid of them, but since they did him no harm, he soon became accustomed to their presence. On investigation he learned that they were serpents-genie, and from that time on began to leave some game for them at the base of the altar.

Once when Da Trang drew near the serpents, he heard a great noise. He went closer and observed that the spotted serpents were being attacked by a larger serpent. Da Trang took up his bow and fired at the latter, wounding it in the head, so that it took flight. One serpent set out in pursuit; but the other had been fatally bitten and died. Da Trang buried the dead serpent behind the shrine.

That night a genie appeared to Da Trang and said: "You saved my life, and you gave my wife an honorable burial. Here is evidence of my gratitude."

With that, Da Trang saw the genie change himself into a serpent. The serpent opened his mouth wide and let fall a beautiful, white pearl.

*   *   *

Da Trang had often heard it said that possession of the pearl of a serpent-genie would permit one to understand the language of the animals. He intended to test this for himself, and next morning, on leaving for the hunt, he placed the pearl in his mouth.

He had hardly entered the forest when he heard a voice which seemed to come from a tree.

"To the right two hundred paces, who sees a deer? To the right two hundred paces, who sees a deer?"

It was the voice of a crow. Da Trang followed the crow's advice, and when he had brought down his prey, the voice continued:

"Do not forget my reward! Do not forget!"

Da Trang asked the crow: "What doest thou wish?"

"The entrails! Only the entrails!" replied the crow.

Da Trang was careful to pay his account. The next day the crow again informed him where he could find a deer, and in this way a close association was formed.

DA TRANG'S CRABS

Da Trang was always careful to deposit his companion's portion of the game in a convenient place.

One day the crow's portion was stolen. And the crow thought that Da Trang had failed to leave his share, and went to his house to complain. The man protested and an argument took place. The crow began to insult Da Trang, who became angered, and fired a poisoned shaft at him. The crow dodged the arrow and flew off to the place where it had fallen; he picked up the arrow in his beak and cried: "Revenge! Revenge!"

Several days later Da Trang was arrested. A poisoned arrow bearing his name had been discovered in the body of a drowned man. In spite of his protests of innocence, he was cast into prison.

One day the jailer was astonished to hear him laugh and speak while alone. When he heard Da Trang chatting with the insects of his cell, he thought him mad. Da Trang would beg the mosquitoes and bugs not to bite him, and would reply to their comments on the quality of the skin of the prisoners who had preceded him.

On a certain occasion Da Trang overheard a conversation between two sparrows who were relating how they emptied several of the royal granaries, which had been poorly guarded. Da Trang immediately asked to see the warden of the prison. Sceptical at first, he investigated and found Da Trang had told the truth.

On another occasion Da Trang questioned some ants who were hastily carrying their eggs and provisions to higher ground. They told him that a great flood was imminent. Da Trang reported this to the warden who hastened to inform the king. The king ordered that the necessary measures be taken. Three days later the waters of the great river mounted rapidly and overflowed, flooding immense regions.

The king then had Da Trang brought to the palace. From his mouth he learned the entire story of the crow's vengeance and the serpent's friendship. Da Trang showed his miraculous pearl. Struck with admiration, the king immediately saw that through the pearl, much could be gained for the general good.

He also hoped to discover for himself the secrets of nature and the miracles of the universe of which men were ignorant. He did not deprive Da Trang of his pearl but kept him near for consultion, and made him repeat all that he heard.

The king was very enthusiastic to hear about the animals' conversations and spent a great deal of time listening to them. He soon perceived that beasts were not as simple as he had believed, and men were wrong to despise them. For they resemble each other, and each species forms an entire world with its own absudities, cruelties, and miseries, quite comparable to those which adorn human societies.

In the hope of making other discoveries, the king took Da Trang with him for long walks along the seashore, where they questioned various kinds of fish.

The king was not long in learning that animals of the earth and inhabitants of the sea often spoke for the sake of speaking, or to foment evil.

DA TRANG'S CRABS

One beautiful spring morning the king and Da Trang went sailing. While Da Trang reclined in the shade of the sail, the king followed the antics of a school of dolphins. Suddenly Da Trang heard a strange sound in the water, and he bent over the side, and saw a cuttlefish swimming alongside the royal barge, singing a joyous air:

"Cloud, white cloud,
  Which floats, slowly floats
  In the blue waters of the sky . . ."

It was so funny to see the cuttlefish singing and rolling in cadence through the waves, that Da Trang burst out laughing. As he did so, the pearl slipped from his mouth and fell into the water.

Da Trang's despair was great, but the king took control of the situation. The location was marked, and the best divers of the kingdom were sent for, but their efforts to find the pearl were in vain.

The king turned to other occupations and seemed to have forgotten the magic pearl, but Da Trang was inconsolable and thought about the lost pearl night and day. He took no interest in life and in spite of the favors of the monarch, wept endlessly over the irretrievable loss.

Always dreaming of finding the lost pearl, Da Trang's weakened brain conceived the idea of filling up the sea.

He assembled an army of workmen who brought hundreds of cartloads of sand to the seashore. The king was at first indulgent, but he finally had to put a stop to these insane efforts.

Da Trang wasted away and died, without recovering his reason. Before death, he had asked to be buried at the very place where he had supervised filling up the sea — the sea that had robbed him of his treasure.

*   *   *

When you are at the seashore, go to the beach early in the morning at ebb tide. You will notice innumerable little balls of sand strewn about the beach. They are the work of Da Trang's crabs, which swarm under your feet, and at the least disturbance disappear into their holes. Using their claws, they rapidly roll the sand into a ball; but a single wave is sufficient to destroy all their work. They are indefatigable however, and are soon at work again amassing another ball, which will only last until the next wave.

It is said that the inconsolable soul of Da Trang has passed to these minute crabs and never ceases to think of the magic pearl and his attempt to fill up the sea.

There is a Vietnamese proverb which is cited whenever a man seems to throw himself into an impossible enterprise, forgetting the limitation of his forces, and the fact that he is only a poor human. It reads:

Da Trang carts his sand into the Eastern Sea;
He grieves and devotes all his energy to no result.

DA TRANG'S CRABS

15

THE JAR OF GOLD

THERE WAS once a poor farmer and his wife, who led a very quiet life in the Vietnamese countryside. Every morning at sun-up he would go to his field and plow until sundown.

The farmer's father before him had done the same, and there would probably be little change in the life of his sons. The farmer thought neither of the past nor even of the future. For him the important thing was simply the completion of each day's task within the allotted time. So he lived from day to day, unconcerned with the ambitions of other men.

One morning as he worked the soil, his foot struck something hard and unyielding. He scraped the dirt from around the object and found an earthen jar. It was heavy and, as he pried it open to see what it contained, many gold coins fell out. He replaced them carefully and again buried the jar at the place where he had found it.

When the farmer returned home that evening he told his wife about the discovery. She was at first elated, but when he told her that he had reburied the gold she became angry.

"Why didn't you bring the jar home?" she exclaimed. "It was a gift from heaven. Someone else will surely find it, and you will have lost it forever!"

The farmer was unconcerned. "If it really is a heavenly gift, no one will take it. If it is not heaven's gift, I don't want it!" he replied.

While the farmer and his wife were engaged in argument, two thieves lurking outside their hut over-heard this conversation in amazement. They then hurried away to the spot which the farmer had des-cribed. They dug away the soil and there rested an earthen jar, just as he had said. The evil men took the jar to their lair, eager to divide the gold.

But when the thieves opened the jar, they found that it contained a family of snakes and not a single gold coin was to be seen. They were furious. They closed the jar and threw it away.

On the following morning the farmer returned to the field as usual and immediately discovered the open hole from which the jar had been removed. This did not disturb him, and he continued to work the field until sundown. On returning home he mentioned to his wife that the jar was missing.

"Of course," she said sarcastically, "who except

THE JAR OF GOLD

you, would leave a jar of gold coins in an open field?"

It so happened that the two thieves were again listening outside the hut. The mention of gold aroused the evil in them, and they now thought of revenging themselves on the poor farmer. They took the jar back to the field and buried it, hoping that the poisonous snakes would bite the unsuspecting man when he opened it again.

On the third day the farmer was surprised to see that the jar had been returned, but he did not touch it. That evening he told his wife of the strange happening.

"One day you find a jar of gold, the next day you lose it, and now you tell me that you have found it again. What am I to believe?" she cried out in exasperation.

The husband assured her that he was speaking the truth.

"Then go back to the field and bring the jar home. It must be a gift from heaven if it has been returned to the field."

"No," replied the husband, "if it is a gift of heaven, it will be sent here without our help."

The two thieves were listening again and their desire for revenge was frightening to behold. They were certain that the farmer and his wife had made fools of them, and intended to teach them a lesson. So they went to the field and brought the jar to the farmer's hut, placing it on his doorstep. Then they hid behind a growth of bamboo to see what would happen.

Early next morning the farmer made his customary

preparations to leave for the field. As he opened the door, he saw the jar on the doorstep. He shouted for his wife who came running. She picked up the jar and gold coins fell from it in torrents.

The two thieves realized that their plans had been thwarted by a higher power, and they stole away.

The farmer and his wife were now wealthy. The woman dressed herself in fine clothes and assumed superior airs. But the advent of sudden wealth did not change the farmer in any way. He continued to labor at the tasks that life had assigned to him in the same way until the day of his death.

THE JAR OF GOLD

16

TRANG TU AND THE DEATH OF HIS WIFE

TRANG TU, the great Chinese teacher who lived during the Chou dynasty, was noted for his wisdom.

When he lost his wife, friends and relatives who had come with ritual offerings for the dead woman found him seated on the floor, legs extended, beating a drum and singing this song:

"Alas! This life is like a flower that forms, then fades.

My wife is dead, so I bury her; if I were dead, she would remarry.

If I had been the first to depart, what a great burst of laughter would have poured forth.

In my fields a new laborer would work; on my horse a strange rider would appear.

My wife would belong to another; my children would have to bear anger and insults.

*When I think of her, my heart tightens; but I look at her
without weeping.*

*The world accuses me of insensibility and remorselessness;
I scoff at the world for nourishing vain griefs.*

*If I could restore the course of things by weeping,
My tears would flow for a thousand autumns without
ceasing."*

Thus sang Trang Tu, without the least sign of regret
or chagrin. Seeing this, his relatives exclaimed:

"What? You two grew old together, and now, not
only do you find no tears for her, you have the heart to
sing and beat your drum."

Then Trang Tu arose and approached his dead wife's
bed. Pointing a finger at her body he said:

"She lies there dead; it isn't that I don't understand. If you insist, I shall weep so that people will
not say that I have been ignorant of the conventions,
but they know nothing of either life or death."

17

WHY DUCKS
SLEEP STANDING
ON ONE LEG

MANY PEOPLE must have wondered why ducks are accustomed to sleep in the funny way that they do—with one leg lifted. The Vietnamese have an interesting explanation for this.

* * *

After Heaven had completed the creation of the world, there were four ducks who found that they only had one leg each. It was difficult for them to walk, and sometimes they were unable to find enough food. They became very morose when they saw how easily other fowls and animals moved about on two legs.

One day the four unfortunate ducks held a meeting and discussed their ignoble condition. They had arrived at a point where life on one leg could no longer be endured, so they decided to lodge a complaint in Heaven. But they were entirely ignorant of Heaven's location, and they did not even know how to draft a petition.

One of them suggested that they should turn to the rooster for help. The others protested that his penmanship was so bad that no one in Heaven would be able to read the petition. But there was no one else to whom they could turn, so after having quacked and grumbled for some time, the four of them went to find the rooster, who was only too eager to help and readily scratched out the desired petition.

The ducks read the petition and then held another meeting to decide which one of them should carry it. The way to Heaven was long and tedious and beset with many pitfalls, so that none of the one-legged ducks was enthusiastic about undertaking the journey.

The rooster, who was standing some distance away, overheard the lively discussion. He coughed discreetly, and approaching the group, delicately asked whether he might be of further service. They were very pleased and accepted his offer to help.

"Not far from here there is a temple," he suggested, looking wisely down his beak, "and it happens that I am acquainted with the god of the place. He could convey your petition to Heaven, and I can give you a letter of introduction to him."

The ducks were loudly grateful, whereupon the rooster put on his spectacles and wrote out a suitably worded letter for them.

The ducks then proceeded to the temple, and as they entered its precincts, they suddenly heard a loud,

WHY DUCKS SLEEP STANDING ON ONE LEG

imperious voice wanting to know why the temple's incense burner had eight legs instead of four. The voice continued by demanding that the four extra legs be removed immediately.

As the ducks heard this, their hopes rose. They did not know what an incense burner was, but they understood that four of its legs were to be removed immediately. They hurried into the temple. The god was still frowning at the incense burner when they entered, and he looked at them unsmilingly.

"Your lordship," said one duck, who had become the spokesman for the group, "here is a letter for you from our friend and neighbor, the rooster, and also our petition. It's about our need of four legs; as you see we have only one leg each."

The god replied that what had been given them at creation was final, and that their petition would serve no purpose. At these words the four ducks fell silent. But then one, younger than the others and more desperate, spoke up and said what was on the minds of all four.

"Your lordship," he stammered, "you spoke just now of removing four legs from the incense burner . . ."

The god looked at him wide-eyed for an instant and then burst into uncontrollable laughter. In the end he agreed to give the ducks the four extra legs.

"But mind you," he said, handing them over to the ducks and winking at the incense burner, "these legs are made of pure gold and are very precious; guard them carefully."

VIETNAMESE LEGENDS

The ducks were ready to promise anything. They took the legs with indescribable joy. They bowed and thanked the god. They attached the extra legs to their bodies and soon they were able to move about like their fellow creatures. But at night when they went to sleep, they would pull up the leg given them by the temple god so that no one could steal it. Other ducks, seeing this, assumed it was the proper way to sleep and in imitation began to lift one leg before retiring for the night. And so the custom has remained to this day.

18

LU SINH'S
DREAM

FOR THE third time Lu Sinh had failed the triennial civil service examinations and it seemed that misfortune followed him every where. Less talented and knowledgeable students were successful and happy.

Sadly Lu Sinh left the capital to return to his native village, his bag of clothing slung over his shoulder at the end of a stick.

In passing through the mountain region of Nam Kha he was caught by a sudden shower, and climbed into a cave to protect himself from the rain. It turned out to be the grotto of an old Taoist hermit.

The hermit invited him to be seated on the only piece of furniture that he owned, a bed of polished stone. Meanwhile he continued to give his attention to a pot of millet porridge that was slowly cooking over the fire. While stirring the millet he asked Lu Sinh whence he had come and where he was going. The latter began by recounting his failures at the government examinations, his intentions of trying again, his hopes and fears. The hermit listened in silence; he then invited Lu Sinh to lie down on the bed to rest for awhile before continuing the journey.

*   *   *

Three years later Lu Sinh was graduated as first doctor of the Empire. Graduation day and those immediately following were days of glory. First came the series of unforgettable rites: his name proclaimed by the herald through his shining copper trumpet to the assembled throng; presentation of his Court robe by a high mandarin; and finally, the ride on a white horse through the capital to his own village, where for several days without interruption, there were banquets and merrymaking.

Following these high public ceremonies came marriage to a princess, the most beautiful daughter of the Emperor. The following years brought the birth of his beautiful children and promotion to the rank of first minister. Having risen rapidly to the pinnacle of wealth and honors, Lu Sinh continued in these functions for fifteen years.

Then barbarians suddenly invaded the Empire. The first battles were disastrous for the Emperor. Lu Sinh, named supreme commander, defeated the enemy, invaded their territory, and killed their king in combat. But the savage charm of the barbarian queen captivated him and he remained with her. Carried away by an overwhelming passion, he forgot completely his wife, his home, his children, and his duty towards Emperor and country.

In vain the Emperor begged Lu Sinh to return to the capital and resume his duties. The Emperor then resolved to send a large army against him. Lu Sinh revolted and tried to meet the forces sent against him, but his own commanders betrayed him into the Emperor's hands. In spite of his wife's pleas for mercy, Lu Sinh was condemned to death by the Emperor.

Lu Sinh spent the night before the execution reliving his entire life: his boyhood poverty, his student labors, his brilliant career, his great happiness, and then the enervating passion, bewilderment, and sudden fall.

* * *

Lu Sinh opened his eyes; he was in the grotto lying on the stone couch. Squatted on the ground near him, an old man was slowly stirring a pot of millet porridge. Only the click of his chopstick on the edge of the pot, hardly more noticeable than the purring of the fire, disturbed the silence of the mountain.

"Young man," said the hermit, "you have had a long sleep, but the porridge is not quite ready. Give me a few minutes more, and I shall invite you to share my modest meal."

19

NGUEN KY AND THE SONGSTRESS

NGUYEN KY'S remarkable intelligence was noticed by everyone while he was still a child. Unfortunately he lost his mother very early in life. His father soon married again and the second wife was extremely severe with her young stepson. She forced him to leave school in order to guard the water buffaloes and to do a man's work in the fields. He had to do the plowing and harrowing, spread the fertilizer, and suffer many insults, hardships, and beatings. His father was so weak in the presence of his wife that he did not dare defend his son. Finally, at the age of fifteen, weary of being ill-fed, poorly dressed, and mistreated, Nguyen Ky decided to leave his father's home.

He wandered for many days without finding work

and was eventually reduced to begging in the streets
for his daily bread.

One day Nguyen Ky presented himself at the door
of an old scholar in the village of Dich Vong, in Ha
Dong province. The scholar was struck by his manly
features and inquired whether he knew how to write.
Nguyen Ky asked for paper and brush and immediately
composed a poem of eight verses in the classical style.

The licentiate could not help admiring the grace and
firmness of the elegant script, but most of all, he was
impressed by the discreet allusions to the young man's
situation and to their meeting. Enchanted with these
eight verses, which demonstrated an unusual erudition
and also revealed a mature and delicate soul, the old
man offered to lodge Nguyen Ky in a cottage near his
home and to give him daily lessons so that he might
continue his education.

Gifted as he was, Nguyen Ky made prodigious
progress. In a few years he was able to make up for all
the time he had lost, and his renown as a scholar
spread throughout the province.

*　　　*　　　*

One spring day, Nguyen Ky and a comrade attended
a festival honoring the village genie. The young scholar
was dressed in a cotton tunic which had been patched
in many places. When he saw himself surrounded by
richly dressed people, his spirits fell and he had no
courage to enter into conversation. He searched for a

corner away from the throng and found a place between the wall and columns of the temple.

Nguyen Ky should not have concerned himself, for the crowd only had eyes for the dazzling beauty of a certain songstress. She was not only beautiful; she also sang admirably. When her lips parted, the notes came forth like precious gems. All the men were enamored and madly competed for her favors. In their generosity, bolts of silken cloth and articles of silver were piled high on a table, as each sought to reward the beauty's charm and delicacy.

Suddenly, during the dance of the lanterns, the young songstress turned slightly as she passed the corner of the temple and perceived Nguyen Ky leaning against a column. She was so startled at his presence that she stopped dead, her eyes fixed on him. She was unable to resume either song or dance.

The next morning Nguyen Ky was reading when he saw the young woman approach his bench. She touched his shoulder in a friendly manner and asked:

"Why is such a talented man so abused by fate?"

She then begged him to accept ten banknotes and several bolts of silk cloth. He tried to refuse but she kept insisting relentlessly. Then she departed so suddenly that Nguyen Ky did not have the opportunity of thanking her properly. He felt ashamed to accept her charity, but he had to admit that he could make good use of this unexpected assistance.

Several days later the songstress again came to his

cottage, and from that time she began to visit him regularly. Each time she would do the housework, mend his clothing, prepare his meals, and encourage him to work, just as if she were his wife.

Notwithstanding this close association, there was no intimacy in their relationship. Nguyen Ky respected her as a dear friend, and in his words and actions he never overstepped the bounds of convention and propriety.

*   *   *

As the songstress and Nguyen Ky become better acquainted, he became more appreciative of her great beauty. One day he was unable to resist placing his arm about her waist. He regretted it almost immediately, for her countenance darkened and she reproached him bitterly.

"Ah! If I were what you take me to be," she said, "I would have only to name my price. Perhaps I should explain why I have chosen you to be my friend. I was thinking of my future. Women in my position do not usually look to the future, and when old age comes they often find themselves destitute and in ill health. That is why I desired to find a superior man on whom I might depend for help later. And now you have chosen to look on me as a flower in the wall or a willow at the side of the road. Must I leave you forever?"

Nguyen Ky understood the significance of these words and he apologized for his thoughtless conduct. From that day onward he fully respected the person of the young woman.

VIETNAMESE LEGENDS

As the date of his examinations approached, Nguyen Ky decided to return to his father's home and to ask him to defray his expenses as a candidate.

At the moment of parting, Nguyen Ky took his dear friend's hand and said:

"It has been my good fortune to meet you during my journey through the miseries of this life. I am deeply in your debt, and that I shall never forget. Before we part, you must tell me how I shall be able to find you when I have passed my examinations and attained my goal."

The young woman replied: "Later, if you have not forgotten me, it will be I who will look for you. But if we are never to meet again, what good is it to know my name and my village? I exact no promise from you; let the world be the judge of our actions."

When Nguyen Ky arrived at his old home, his father's joy was great indeed, for he had not expected to see his son again. The stepmother was also very attentive towards the young scholar who seemed destined to win such brilliant success. And as expected, Nguyen Ky passed the preliminary provincial examination, and then gained first place in the triennial regional competition.

*   *   *

Nguyen Ky's father now thought that it was time for him to marry, and he proposed a young maiden who belonged to an excellent family. Nguyen Ky at first first refused to do his father's bidding. He told the story of his benefactress, affirming that he preferred to die rather than to betray her confidence. But his explanations were weak, and his father failed to comprehend the full significance of the unusual relationship. He was certain that it had been only a banal adventure and that Nguyen Ky would soon forget the woman. The father thought that he had done very well in opposing his son's wishes and stated that he would never receive a songstress into his home.

Nguyen Ky suffered a great deal in this uncomfortable situation. His love and esteem for the young woman were sincere, and he felt that he ought not abandon her, even though they had exchanged no vows. But these considerations did not make him forget that a man has other duties, less romantic perhaps, but more imperious, from which he cannot escape. And, in the end, he obeyed his father.

* * *

The following year Nguyen Ky returned to the capital for the doctoral examinations. The young woman immediately came to visit him, bringing him all sorts of presents. Seeing his constraint, she guessed the reason behind it and said:

"I understand; there is no need to speak. It is the working of fate. Each of us must travel his own road, in different directions."

And she said farewell.

* * *

That year Nguyen Ky was awarded the doctoral degree. He was then named mandarin in the imperial cabinet and soon departed with an embassy to China. On his return, he occupied high offices in the provinces and in the capital for the next ten years. When the agitator Cau revolted in Hai Duong, Nguyen Ky was sent against him. He pacified the region and for this service obtained the title of duke.

He had now reached the summit of his career. Riches, honors, and a numerous progeny were his. He could desire nothing more. Occasionally, when his friends made allusion to his difficult years as a student, he would be overcome with emotion and would secretly reproach himself for his conduct. Several times he employed servants to find the songstress, but she had disappeared and left no trace.

One evening at the home of the Marquis Dang, Nguyen Ky noticed a certain woman seated among the musicians and entertainers. Her features reminded him strangely of a face that he should know. He inquired and learned that it was indeed his friend of yesteryear.

Although her beauty had already faded from the dust and wind of this world, the voice and manners had lost nothing of their freshness and charm. From his position Nguyen Ky imagined that he was witnessing an apparition from the years of his youth.

Nguyen Ky leaned from his friend, that ten years previously she had married a soldier from Thai Nguyen. He had died and she had not remarried. She had accumulated some savings which would have permitted her to take care of her aged mother. Unfortunately, a younger brother had squandered everything so that she had been obliged to take her mother with her to the capital in order to earn their daily bowl of rice.

Deeply moved by this meeting and the tale of necessity, Nguyen Ky invited his old friend and her mother to live in his home. She accepted in deference to her mother. The two women were allotted a section of the house and their every want was ministered to.

Some months later the old woman died. Nguyen Ky saw to it that she was given a decent burial.

When the funeral was over, his friend came to thank him and to beg permission to leave his home. Unable to hold her further, he begged her to accept some money. She refused. He wanted to speak to her of the past, but it was too difficult. Seeing her on the point of leaving forever, he felt a lump rise in his throat. And he was overcome with a melancholy that he had not experienced in a long, long time.

20

THE TOAD
IS HEAVEN'S
UNCLE

WHEN HEAVEN was close to Earth long, long ago, and all the animals spoke with human voices, a terrible drought descended upon the Earth. It lasted many months, and all the rivers, lakes, ponds, streams, and wells went dry.

Among the Earth's diverse inhabitants there was an ugly toad who lived near a pond. He saw the pond shrinking in size from day to day and finally determined to do something about it. He did not relish a slow, lingering death which seemed inevitable. After thinking it over for some time, the toad decided that the only course was to go directly to Heaven and interest the gods in what was happening on Earth.

Alone, he set off on the long journey.

The toad had traveled only a few miles when he met a group of honey bees and stopped to chat with them. During the conversation he told them of his resolve to seek the King of Heaven's help. The bees were enthusiastic about his venture, for they too were seeing bad times; without the flowers there was no honey at all. They decided to join the toad and together the party set out.

When the bees and the toad had continued for some distance, they came upon a cock who was in very low spirits. The harvest had been affected by the drought and there was no grain or insects. It was quite easy for the toad and the bees to convince the cock that he would have nothing to lose by joining forces.

The enlarged party had hardly resumed the journey, when they encountered an ill-tempered tiger. He was especially angry because the drought was killing all the game on which he had been accustomed to prey. He too became a member of the party. Soon a fox and a bear joined up. The group journeyed on, inspired by the worthy purpose that had brought them all together.

After many days of jumping from star to star the party arrived at Tien Dinh, the very Gates of Heaven. The toad asked the others to remain outside until he called them. Then he hopped through the gates and into the palace. He crossed the polished floors of many empty chambers and finally entered the impressive Hall of Audience. Laughter was audible from somewhere inside, and the toad made his way toward the sound.

Finally he came to a room where the King of Heaven was seated at a table playing cards with a number of angels and fairies. The toad was very indignant to see them engaged in this idle pastime. Inhaling deeply, his bulging eyes wide open, he leapt in a great high hop to land plop in the middle of the players. There was a stunned silence as the smile gradually left the King of Heaven's face. He frowned angrily and spoke in a thundering tone.

"Insolent toad," he roared, "how dare you defile our august company?"

Now the toad, who had already faced death on Earth, did not flinch a bit. He had a quiet courage that comes from extreme desperation.

"Your Majesty," he began, but could say no more.

"What?" shouted the King of Heaven. "How dare you speak in my presence?"

At that moment the guards rushed in, intending to throw the toad out. But a toad is not so easily captured. He hopped away from the guards and called aloud for the bees, who swarmed in and attacked the guards, who retreated in panic to avoid being stung.

The King of Heaven watched these proceedings in utter amazement. Then he called on the Thunder God to silence the insolent toad, but the cock was more than a match for that deity. The King of Heaven then called for the Captain of the Hounds, but the tiger took care of him and the bear and the fox ripped the stomachs of the dogs. Slowly a look of great respect came to the eyes of the King of Heaven and a reasonableness entered his mind.

"Sire," said the toad, "my friends and I came here

THE TOAD IS HEAVEN'S UNCLE

respectfully, to bring to your celestial attention the sad plight of the inhabitants of the Earth. There has been no rain for many months, the river-beds have dried up and the fields are parched. Animals are dying everywhere and all the plants have wilted. Sire, we must have rain."

"Yes," nodded the King of Heaven, and added "uncle," so overpowered had he been with the toad's personality. And he promised to look into the matter immediately.

The celestial sluices opened and rain came at last to the Earth. But by that time three-fourths of the population were dead. Some animals of each species survived however, and soon new generations began to populate the earth again. Life was reborn in every corner of the earth.

So that a similar expedition of earthly beings would not again appear in his palace, the King of Heaven told the toad: "From now on, it will not be necessary to make such a long trip with your friends. If there is a drought in the future or whenever you need rain, remain there on Earth and simply call me."

Since that time the toad, "Heaven's uncle," and his progeny have watched over the Earth's supply of water and have never failed to croak loudly and effectively whenever rain is needed.

When the toad died, his sons and the other animals built a fitting memorial to his memory, and they began to commemorate the day on which he made his heroic journey to Heaven. Thus, the toad's great deed is remembered to this day in Vietnam, and the expression "the toad is Heaven's uncle" has entered Vietnamese parlance.

21

THACH SANH

ONCE UPON a time, in the Cao Bang district of Vietnam, there lived an old woodman and his wife. The woodman's name was Thach. Although they had been married for many years, they were still childless; this was a great sorrow for them both.

The woodman and his wife did everything possible to make themselves useful to the other people of the village, always hoping that Heaven would have mercy on them and favor them with a child.

The fame of their virtue and self-sacrifice soon spread throughout the realm. It even reached the ears of the Emperor of Jade, the Ruler of Heaven. Prompted by their virtue, he decided to bless the couple. One of his own children was commanded to descend to earth and attach himself to Thach's family as a son.

Thach's wife then conceived, but not in the manner

of an ordinary mortal. The period of nine months passed and she did not give birth. A year passed, then two. When the woman had been pregnant for almost three years the woodman became ill, and died. A few months after her husband's death, the woman bore a vigorous and healthy male child, whom she named Thach Sanh.

Several years later the old woman also passed away, and from then on, the young orphan lived alone in his cabin at the foot of an old banyan tree. He had only a loincloth with which to clothe himself and an axe with which to cut wood. He followed in the profession of his father and continued to earn his daily rice by falling trees and cutting timber. Sometimes, when the weather was too severe and he was unable to work in the forest, he was forced to live on moss and wild berries. He had only spring water to quench his thirst.

Thach Sanh was almost thirteen years of age, when one day, while returning to his cabin with a full load of wood on his back, he saw an old man seated at the foot of the spreading banyan.

"Who are you, respected grandfather?" he inquired.

The old man replied, "I am the genie Ly Tinh. The Emperor of Jade has sent me here to instruct you in the use of magical powers which will be of help to you during your earthly life."

When the diligent youth had finally mastered the use of the magical powers, the genie bade farewell and disappeared in the clouds.

Having committed to memory all the secrets that he

had been told, Tach Sanh continued his modest way of life, never forgetting the pious worship of his parents.

One day, a wandering brandy merchant named Ly Thong stopped at Thach Sanh's cabin to rest. On observing the sturdy youth he immediately planned to exploit him. He began to ask Thach Sanh about his family and seemingly took pity on him. Ly Thong invited the orphan to share his home, proposing that they live as brothers.

"We will live together with my old mother," he said.

The unsuspecting orphan willingly consented and went with Ly Thong to his home. Ly Thong's mother at once perceived the profit that she could gain from his labor; so she welcomed Thach Sanh and accepted him as her son.

*   *   *

At that time, there lived a cruel monster that ate human flesh, and the authorities had been ordered to destroy it. However, the moster was endowed with miraculous powers, and could not be injured. Resignedly, the king was compelled to build a temple in the monster's honor, where every year a young man of the village was sacrificed.

It happened that Ly Thong was chosen as the intended sacrificial victim that year. When informed of this he was seized with terror. With his mother, he secretely plotted to send the naive and guileless Thach Sanh to the sacrificial altar in his stead.

They first arranged a solemn feast. As soon as Thach Sanh arrived home, carrying a load of wood, they begged him to cease working and invited him to partake of food and wine. Thach Sanh was surprised, but Thong reassured him, saying, "Do not worry, brother; today we are celebrating the anniversary of of my father's death."

Thach Sanh accepted the invitation and ate his fill. At the close of the meal Ly Thong spoke again.

"I have a favor to ask of you," he said. "By royal command I have been chosen to stand guard at the temple tonight. Unfortunately, I have already made preparations to distill brandy and my absence tonight would certainly bring ruin to my business. Will you be kind enough to stand guard in my place?"

Thach Sanh had no reason to doubt the truth of this story and immediately agreed. Soon afterwards, he set out for the temple.

When he arrived, the forest was completely silent and drowned in utter darkness. Suddenly, a strong current of air shook the trees, the atmosphere cooled sharply, and with a tremulous hiss, the great monster appeared, fire spouting from its mouth. It lunged at Thach Sanh, but the latter was ready. With his magical powers he fought against the monster and finally brought it to the ground. The monster then transformed itself into a serpent. Thach Sanh cut off its head with his axe, and taking it in his hands, returned home.

On reaching the door of the house he called out. Ly Thong and his mother thought it could only be Thach Sanh's spirit, which had returned to avenge him.

They fell prone, and humbly begged for pardon from all the gods of heaven. Only then did Thach Sanh clearly understand the perfidy of his adopted mother and brother. But he was so good at heart that he felt no anger towards them. When the old woman opened the door, he told them how he had killed the monster and showed them its head. On hearing this, Ly Thong thought up a new and still more evil plan.

"How terrible!" he exclaimed. "The serpent was a near relative of the king and greatly beloved by him. If you have really killed it, you will certainly be condemned to death for the deed."

In consternation Thach Sanh knelt before Ly Thong, and begged for his help.

"Leave here at once," the false brother advised, "we will take care of everything."

Thach Sanh quickly thanked mother and son and fled to the forest. He returned to his old cabin under the banyan tree and took refuge there.

Ly Thong then went to the royal palace with the serpent's head and reported to the king that it was he who had killed the serpent. The king was elated to hear of this heroic deed and praised him exceedingly, naming him commander-in-chief of the royal armies.

Thenceforth the son and his abominable mother lived in great luxury and enjoyed all the honors of the court. On the other hand, the unfortunate Thach Sanh was subjected to the miserable existence of a woodman in his cabin under the thick foilage of the banyan tree.

VIETNAMESE LEGENDS

*　*　*

The king had only one child, the Princess Quynh Nga, who was famous for her flowerlike beauty. She was as mild and delicate as celestial perfume, and the king loved her with all his heart.

The princess had reached a marriageable age, and heralds were dispatched throughout the realm, announcing that the king had decided to invite all prospective suitors to a banquet, where the princess would select her future husband.

When informed of this event, the handsome princes of many kingdoms came in great numbers, with numerous retainers. The common people also flocked to the capital city, taking advantage of the occasion for a glimpse of the beautiful princess.

As soon as all the suitors had assembled and the king was seated on his golden throne, the princess was asked to appear.

She was truly beautiful to see, but appeared inattentive and listless. After looking around for some time, her face showed more displeasure than before.

"Whom have you chosen?" inquired the king.

"Alas!" replied the princess. "Fate has dealt unkindly with me, dear father. I beg you, do not marry me to any of these."

The king was greatly disappointed, but he loved his daughter so dearly that he could not force her to make a choice. The princess returned to her chamber, where she spent long, melancholic days. Would the young man of whom she so often dreamed never come forth?

THACH SANH

As the days passed the princess ceased to comb her hair and attend to her appearance. She never left her palace. There she passed the time in drawing pictures of birds and flowers and in composing verses. But more often than not, she would plunge herself into fantastic dreams, after which she would weep inconsolably.

One day, when she and her maids were strolling in the royal gardens, a giant eagle suddenly appeared in the sky. It swooped down and seized the princess in its cruel talons, flying off to the mountains. The maids were struck with terror and fell in a faint.

The monstrous eagle flew across the forest in which Thach Sanh was dwelling. As he sat at the foot of the big banyan, he suddenly saw the great bird fly over, the young woman a prisoner in its claws. He aimed his crossbow at the bird and wounded it in the left wing. Nevertheless, by virtue of its magical powers, the eagle was able to withdraw the arrow from its flesh and continue the flight. Thach Sanh ran after the eagle, following its bloody trail. Finally he reached the entrance to a deep cavern where man had never explored.

The mammoth eagle had already disappeared from sight. Taking note of the location of the cavern, Thach Sanh returned home.

When the king learned of the princess' abduction, he was plunged in sorrow. He immediately ordered Ly Thong to organize a search party and promised to give him his daughter in marriage and even to grant him his throne, if he should succeed in saving her. Ly Thong rejoiced to hear this offer, but at the same time he was very disquieted, for he did not know how to begin the search.

"Just where did that cruel monster take the princess?" he wondered.

After meditating for several days and nights, he finally decided to organize a ten-day festival, to which he would invite all the citizens of the land. He hoped that from the mouths of all these guests he would learn something about the location of the eagle's lair.

Nine days passed and the festivities were already drawing to a close, but no one had said a single word about the cruel bird and its whereabouts.

On the tenth and last day of the festival, Thach Sanh was informed by some villagers that a great affair had been organized in the capital, by the mandarin Ly Thong. He went there and was immediately noticed by Ly Thong, who greeted him warmly, hoping to draw some information from him.

Thach Sanh told Ly Thong the entire story of the eagle's bloody flight and how he had tracked it to the cavern. Ly Thong was naturally very pleased.

"If you help me in this grave matter," he promised, "we will both enjoy great honors and riches, and our family will be proud of you."

Flattered by these words, Thach Sanh offered to guide him to the cavern. With great joy Ly Thong ordered them to prepare a feast in honor of the brave Thach Sanh.

On the following day the search party set out in full regalia. Protected from the sun's burning rays by a large parasol, Ly Thong rode forth on his beautiful steed. In the lead, barefoot and shirtless, Thach Sanh opened the way.

After a difficult march, they reached the cavern on the second day. Thach Sanh told Ly Thong his plan.

"The cavern is very deep," he said. "I will have to go down alone on a rope. When I jerk the rope three times, you must pull it up, for that will mean that the princess is tied to it. Then let the rope down again so I can make my escape."

The rope was let down and Thach Sanh descended into the depths of the cavern, where he found the princess. He told her that he had come to take her back to the capital. The princess was deeply moved and unable to hide her emotions.

"My savior and my lord!" she exlaimed. "I thank you a thousand times for your sacrifice."

After a brief pause, she continued: "Please take me to be your wedded wife. We will arrange the wedding ceremony immediately after our return to the palace."

Completely taken aback, Thach Sanh finally found words to reply: "I am sorry," he said, "but it is impossible. I have come here at the king's command and as Ly Thong has wished. If I were to accept your proposal, I would prove false to my trust."

"Do not fear," replied the princess. "I have made my decision, and I can persuade my father to respect my wishes."

Thach Sanh found no words with which to reply. He then inquired about the eagle.

"It is very badly wounded in the left wing and is lying on a bed at the end of the cavern," she replied, pointing to a path that led towards the very depths of the dark cave.

Thach Sanh then produced a white tablet and told the princess to dissolve it in some water and offer it to the eagle to drink.

"It will render the bird unconscious," he said, "and we will be free to make our escape."

The princess prepared the potion and went to the eagle's bed. It was very thirsty and gladly accepted the drink that the princess offered. As soon as the drug had taken effect, the eagle fell into a deep sleep. Then Thach Sanh tied the princess to the rope and jerked it three times. On receiving this signal, Ly Thong began to pull upward on the rope, and the princess soon came to the surface.

While Thach Sanh was in the cavern, Ly Thong had conceived a diabolical plan. He commanded his companions to return to the palace with the princess.

"All of you return," he said. "I will take care of the great brute myself. Your presence here would only hinder me. Leave at once."

The terrified servants were only too happy to obey the order. When they had departed, Ly Thong moved a large rock to the cavern entrance, thus blocking the passage, and barring the unfortunate Thach Sanh's return to the external world. That accomplished, the treacherous mandarin returned to the palace.

*　　*　　*

Thach Sanh was very uneasy when he found that the entrance to the cavern had been blocked. At the same time the eagle regained consciousness. It called loudly for the princess, and when it found that she had escaped, became furious. Even greater was its anger, when it saw that instead of the princess, there was a strange man in the cavern.

The eagle screeched so loudly that the cavern walls trembled, but Thach Sanh quickly turned to his magical powers and attacked the wounded bird. The battle was long and furious. Only after more than a hundred blows with his woodman's axe, was he finally able to silence the monster.

Then Thach Sanh felt his way along the high walls towards the exit. Suddenly, he came upon an iron cage in a secluded corner of the cavern. A handsome youth was seated in the cage.

"Who are you?" demanded Thach Sanh. "How did you come to be imprisoned here?"

"I am the son of the Sea King," replied the captive. "One year ago, when I was walking on land to admire the beautiful scenery of nature, an eagle-monster swooped down on me and brought me here. Now that you have found me, I behold my savior! If you will free me from the clutches of this monster, I shall never forget your deed."

Touched to the heart by this sad story, Thach Sanh aimed his crossbow and fired an arrow at the cage, which immediately broke apart.

Freed from his imprisonment, the young sea prince

knelt before his benefactor and invited him to accompany him to the Palace of the Waters, so that the Sea King could personally reward him for the great service that he had rendered.

On the way, the sea prince said to Thach Sanh, "My father is certain to offer you gold and gems, but do not accept them! Accept only the magic lute that was once given to him by the Emperor of Jade. This lute's music will give you the power to overcome every danger. It is quite possible that you will have need of it in the future."

At last they reached the Palace of the Waters, where every species of fish rejoicingly welcomed them.

The Sea King was of course overjoyed to see his kidnapped son, for he had despaired of ever finding him alive. The prince related his many experiences and introduced Thach Sanh as his savior. The Sea King then commanded his servants to prepare a great banquet in honor of the famous guest.

"I do not know how to show my deep gratitude for your valorous services to my son, the prince," he said to Thach Sanh.

"Father," interrupted the son, "only the magic lute would be a worthy reward."

The king agreed without hesitation. Thach Sanh received the gift with great emotion. After the banquet he expressed the desire to return to land.

"Go whenever you wish!" replied the Sea King, and commanded the waves to open, and asked the Genie of the Waters to escort the brave Thach Sanh to land.

THACH SANH

Thach Sanh then returned to his cabin and experimented in the use of his new magical powers.

The big banyan tree, which had seemed to wither and grow old during his absence, now seemed to revive; its leaves turned green again, as if to greet the master's return. When a tree can show such fidelity, why must man prove so thankless to his benefactors?

*   *   *

At court, Ly Thong told how he had rescued the princess and waited impatiently for the king to fulfill his promises to give him his daughter in marriage, and and then his very throne.

"I will keep my promise," said the king, "but my daughter still has the right to decide her future. If she consents, the wedding will take place immediately."

When Princess Quynh Nga learned that Ly Thong had taken the credit for her rescue on himself, and was behaving with such faithlessness toward his friend and brother, she suddenly lost her power of speech.

The king was very distressed at this turn of events and commanded that a temple be built where offerings would be made to Heaven, in the hope that Heaven would relent.

Ceremonies lasted an entire month but without result. The areca nuts and the betel leaves on the altar dried and withered, but the princess' red lips remained sealed.

*   *   *

After the eagle's death, its restless spirit began to wander through the land, begging alms by day and

stealing the domesticated fowls of the villagers at night.
One night, quite by chance, this spirit met the spirit
of the serpent-monster that had also been killed by
Thach Sanh. These two evil spirits became friends and
together they plotted revenge.

"It seems to me," said the serpent-spirit, "that we
should force our way into the royal treasury and steal
the royal pearls and diamonds. We will bury them
beneath the banyan tree at Thach Sanh's cabin. Then
we will expose the theft, and he will not be able to
avoid royal punishment."

The eagle-spirit laughed at this clever plot and
agreed. The two spirits then broke into the treasury,
stole the jewels, and buried them as planned.

In searching for the king's stolen jewels, the guards
one day arrived at Thach Sanh's cabin. He was
sleeping soundly at the foot of the banyan tree, at the
very place where the spirits had buried the treasure.
The guards found the treasure and accused Thach
Sanh of the theft. His hands were bound together and
a yoke was placed about his neck. He was confident
that he could prove his innocence however, and therefore asked to be taken to the palace.

Instead of taking him to the palace, the guards threw
him into prison and subjected him to torture. The
warden ordered the guards to confiscate all his possessions — his axe, his crossbow and arrows, and the
magic lute. When the guards attempted to seize the
axe and the crossbow, they were thrown to the ground.
Furious, the warden himself tried to take away the

lute but, before he could touch it, the pupils of his eyes exploded and he was blinded.

When Ly Thong was informed of these happenings, he feared Thach Sanh's revenge. He decided that he must get rid of him forever and therefore condemned him to death.

Meanwhile, Thach Sanh took advantage of a suitable moment to ask the guards the name of their captain. They informed him that it was none other than Ly Thong himself. Instead of venting his anger, Thach Sanh took up his lute and began to play. He was greatly surprised when the instrument responded to the touch of his fingers and in plaintive tones related the entire story of Ly Thong's cruel work. Great was his unhappiness and disgust at the crimes committed by his one-time friend and brother. The lute continued to weep and lament, and its echo resounded from palace to palace. Its mournful tones even penetrated the private chambers of the princess.

Princess Quynh Nga was lost in unhappy revery when she was awakened by the sound of the lute. At once she arose as vigorous and refreshed as a rose of spring. She suddenly regained her power of speech and went at once to the court. With words and laughter she begged the king to invite the lute player to the royal palace.

Astonished at hearing his daughter speak again, the king asked: "Who is the owner of the lute which has the magic power of giving back the faculty of speech?"

"He is Thach Sanh, my true savior, dear father,"

replied the princess. "When I met him for the first time in that dark cavern, I promised to marry him. But the pitiless Ly Thong blocked the entrance to the cavern, jealous of gaining honors for himself, which only the brave Thach Sanh has the right and privilege to enjoy. His absence was the reason for my silence."

Thus informed of the truth, the king at once ordered his attendants to escort Thach Sanh to the palace.

Seeing him in chains, the princess was unable to control her emotions. She burst into tears, remembering their meeting in the cavern. Thach Sanh was greatly moved. In reply to the king's questions he told in detail all that had happened. He described how he had been left an orphan in his early years; how he had been instructed by the genie in the use of magical powers; how he had become a brother to Ly Thong; how he had beheaded the serpent; how he had wounded the eagle and found the princess; how he had been able to free the son of the Sea King; and finally how the monster-spirits had plotted against him.

When the king had heard the entire story, he commanded the guards to unchain the prisoner. He then ordered fine raiment for him and commanded his stewards to prepare a great feast in his honor. As the celebration reached its peak, the king announced that Thach Sanh had been named duke and as the king's son-in-law, he would command the royal armies.

As for the malicious Ly Thong and his mother, they were arrested by royal command and imprisoned. The king gave Thach Sanh full power to judge and sentence

THACH SANH

them. He was in no revengeful mood, however, and pardoned the evildoers and begged them to return to their native village and lead a quiet life. The faithless man and his mother were en route home when a sudden storm began to rage, and both were killed by lightning. Ly Thong was then changed into a cockroach spirit.

The wedding of Thach Sanh and the Princess Quynh Nga was arranged with great pomp and ceremony. The princes of all the surrounding states, who had unsuccessfully competed for the princess' hand, were very angry when they learned that the princess had married a common man. They sent their armies against the kingdom. But Thach Sanh soon defeated the invaders, all of whom surrendered unconditionally.

When the old king abdicated in favor of Thach Sanh, the princes and high officials of the eighteen vassal states, as well as the entire aristocracy of the realm, arrived to take part in the coronation ceremonies.

The new sovereign abolished many taxes and duties, amnestied prisoners, and stimulated the cultivation of rice and the culture of silk throughout the land.

After their marriage, Thach Sanh and Quynh Nga lived in perfect happiness. Their union was soon blessed with a handsome boy-child, who was born in the second autumn of their conjugal life.

Under their rule the kingdom enjoyed peace and prosperity, and for many years the land rejoiced at the kind hearts and compassion of the reigning monarchs.

22

THE COOK'S
BIG FISH

TU SAN of the land of the Trinh considered himself a disciple of Confucius.

One day his cook was enticed into a game of chance, and lost the money that had been entrusted to him for the day's purchases at the market. Fearful of being punished should he return home with empty hands, he invented the following story.

"This morning on arriving at the market, I noticed a large fish for sale. It was fat and fresh — in short, a superb fish. For the sake of curiosity I asked the price. It was only one bill, although the fish was easily worth two or three. It was a real bargian and thinking only of the fine dish that it would make for you, I did not hesitate to spend the money for today's provisions.

"Halfway home, the fish, which I was carrying on a line through the gills, began to stiffen as in death. I recalled the old adage: 'A fish out of water is a dead fish,' and as I happened to be passing a pond, I made haste to plunge it into the water, hoping to revive it under the influence of its natural element.

"A moment later, seeing it was still lifeless, I took it off the line and held it in my two hands. Soon it stirred a little, yawned, and then with a quick movement slipped from my grasp. I plunged my arm into the water to seize it again, but with a flick of the tail it was gone. I confess that I have been very stupid."

When the cook had finished his tale, Tu San clapped his hands and said: "That's perfect! That's perfect!"

He was thinking of the fish's bold escape.

But the cook failed to understand this point and left, laughing up his sleeve. Then he went about telling his friends with a triumphant air:

"Who says my master is so wise? I lost all the market money at cards. Then I invented a story, and he swallowed it whole. Who says my master is so wise?"

Mencius, the philosopher, once said "A plausible lie can deceive even a superior intellect."

23

A PERFECT FRIENDSHIP

DUONG LE was a poor student who had to work hard as a common laborer in order to finance his studies. On the other hand, his friend, Luu Binh, had inherited a small fortune and seemed well-situated for life. When Luu Binh learned that Duong Le's studies were suffering because of the long hours of work he determined to invite him to live at his home until the triennial examination.

Thereafter, the two friends shared the same food and studied beneath the light of the same lamp.

As often happens, Duong Le was conscious of his needy situation and worked hard, spending long nights in study. Luu Binh became over-confident because of the security of wealth and ceased to study as before.

When the examinations were held, Duong Le received the degree of *cu nhan,* as expected, and was appointed mandarin. Luu Binh failed.

The wealthy young man returned home despondently. In his despair he gave himself up to self-indulgence and recklessly squandered his fortune. In desperation he tried the examinations again, but again met with failure.

Recalling that Duong Le was in charge of one of the district administrations in the area, he swallowed his pride and turned to him for assistance. Imagine his chagrin when Duong Le not only refused to receive him, but ordered his guards to drive him away. Luu Binh trudged on, his small bundle of possessions at the end of a stick. His weary gait and downcast mien told the story of a man's failure in life.

That night Luu Binh arrived at a small roadside inn and made the acquaintance of the mistress, a comely young woman named Chau Long. She welcomed him with a cup of steaming tea and listened sympathetically as Luu Binh recounted the long story of his failures. Chau Long encouraged him to try again. She suggested that he remain at the inn and promised to help him in every way possible.

Freed from the temptations of excessive wealth, Luu Binh devoted himself exclusively to his studies. The tender days passed quickly and the time for the examinations approached. When the results were published, Luu Binh's name was at the top of the list. He returned to the inn with the good news, but to his dismay Chau Long had disappeared. He searched for her everywhere, but she was not to be found. Finally, the new mandarin resigned himself to unhappiness and departed for his post.

Many years passed until one day, in the execution of his duties, Luu Binh happened to be passing through the district of his old friend, Duong Le. The memory of his friend's ingratitude did not prevent him from paying a visit. This time Duong Le welcomed his fellow mandarin with great pleasure and offered him tea. As they were drinking and talking, a woman entered the reception room. She approached the two men smiling.

Consternation and astonishment crossed Luu Binh's face, for in the woman he recognized Chau Long, the supposed mistress of the inn. Duong Le then explained to his old friend that to have helped him openly would have produced no reform. Therefore he had sent his own wife to encourage and aid him, until he would pass the examinations. He had been willing to make this sacrifice in the name of friendship.

And that is why people in Vietnam nod understandably and refer to the example of Duong Le and Luu Binh whenever they hear the story of a deep, unbreakable friendship.

A PERFECT FRIENDSHIP

24

KHUAT NGUYEN
AND THE
FISHERMAN

SOMETIME after he was exiled from the Court, Khuat Nguyen was strolling along the edge of a lake and singing to himself. His face had grown thin and his figure lean.

An old fisherman saw him and asked:

"Is it you My Lord of Tam Lu? Tell me why you were dismissed from the Court."

Khuat Nguyen replied:

"In a soiled world, my hands alone were clean; all others were drunk, and I alone was sober. That is why I was dismissed."

The fisherman then said:

"The wise man is never obstinate; he is able to adjust to the circumstances. If the world is soiled, why not stir up the turbid waters? If men are drunk, why not take a bit of alcohol, or even vinegar, and drink along with them. Why try to force your ideas on others, only to arrive where you are now?"

Khuat Nguyen replied:

"I have heard it said, 'When thou hast just washed thy hair, do not put on a dirty hat.' My body is clean, how could I endure impure contacts? I would throw myself into the waters of the Tuong as food for the fish, rather than see my purity soiled by the dirt of the world."

The old fisherman smiled while rowing away. Then he began to sing:

"The limipid waters of the river Tuong roll by
And I wash my clothes therein.
But should these waters be turbid,
I would wash only my feet"

His song ended, he left, saying nothing more.

25

THE GOLDEN
TORTOISE

GREAT-HEART and Perfect-Nobility had been friends since childhood. Great-Heart was rich and Perfect-Nobility was poor.

One day Great-Heart said to Perfect-Nobility:

"You lack the necessary funds to set up a business. Let us advance you enough capital for a beginning, and you can pay us back when you are able."

Perfect-Nobility reflected for a long time:

"I should accept," he said to himself, "these friends are kind and sincere. But if I fail in my enterprise, how will I be able to pay off the debt?"

He consulted his wife. She shared his scruples, and the two were unanimous in their decision to refuse the offer and resign themselves to a lifetime of poverty.

* * *

The next day Perfect-Nobility went to the home of his friend.

"I thank my brother and sister," he said, "but truly I do not know what kind of business I could go into. I cannot accept your money."

During the conversation, Great-Heart showed his guest a golden tortoise that he had had cast from all the precious metal he and his wife possessed. They chatted awhile, drank tea together, and then dozed off.

While they were asleep, Great-Heart's son entered the room. He saw the golden tortoise on the table and carried it out of the room, intending to play with it. Later, he left for a neighboring village without returning the tortoise.

Shortly after the two friends awoke. Perfect-Nobility took leave of his friend without either of them observing that the golden tortoise had disappeared.

*   *   *

As soon as Great-Heart noticed that the golden tortoise was gone he questioned his wife about the matter. She replied that she had not touched the tortoise. He did not know what to think, but not for a moment was Perfect-Nobility under suspicion.

When Great-Heart and Perfect-Nobility met on the following day, the former said:

"Did you by any chance take our golden tortoise to show to your wife? Please keep it as long as you like."

Perfect-Nobility and his wife were thus placed in a cruelly embarrassing situation. "We are poor," they

THE GOLDEN TORTOISE

said to each other, "if we say that we do not have the tortoise, others will be under suspicion. We must spare our friends this misfortune."

Perfect-Nobility and his wife sold the few goods that they possessed and went to knock at the door of the richest landlord of the region, Generous-Opulence, the owner of immense paddy fields. They threw themselves at his feet and begged him to take them into his service for life, in exchange for the quantity of gold needed to cast another golden tortoise, which they could deliver to Great-Heart.

As soon as he had heard their story, Generous-Opulence obtained the necessary gold and gave it to the goldsmith who had manufactured the original tortoise. Thus everything was done in accordance with the wishers of Perfect-Nobility and his wife. However Generous-Opulence did not demand that they remain in his service. On their part, Perfect-Nobility and his wife refused to leave and remained in the home of their benefactor, "in order to wait on him hand and foot."

*   *   *

Sometime later Great-Heart's son returned the golden tortoise to the room and was surprised to see a second tortoise there.

"Papa! Mama!" he cried as soon as he had seen it. "You thought it was lost! Fortunately I took it!"

The parents were completely dumbfounded. Of the two tortoises which was really theirs? And whence came the other?

Having suspected the truth, Great-Heart hastened

to the home of Perfect-Nobility. He found the house
deserted. The neighbors told him that his friends had
sold themselves into the service of Generous-Opulence
and could be found in the latter's home.

Emotionally touched, Great-Heart ran there as fast
as he could. He sent for Perfect-Nobility and the two
friends burst into tears and embraced heartily.

Great-Heart desired to deliver the second tortoise
into the hands of Generous-Opulence in order to
redeem his friends' freedom.

But Generous-Opulence answered him thusly:

"You have borrowed nothing from me; therefore
there is no question of returning anything. As for your
two friends, I have never commanded them to remain
here. You do not have to redeem them; they have
never ceased to be free."

It was impossible to arrive at an agreement. Generous-Opulence would not accept the gold that he had
given them. Perfect-Nobility and his wife considered
themselves indentured and refused to leave the service
of Generous-Opulence. Great-Heart did not wish to
keep that which did not belong to him.

Finally, they found it necessary to refer the case to
the mandarin. We do not know his decision.

THE GOLDEN TORTOISE

26

THE
STOLEN VASE

IN A CERTAIN Buddhist temple, it was found that a golden vase had disappeared after a sacrifice to Heaven. Suspicion pointed to a cook who had been standing near it during the ceremony. After being tortured, he admitted the theft, and declared that he had buried it in the temple courtyard.

The cook was taken to the courtyard and ordered to indicate the exact spot. The area was dug up but nothing was found. The cook was sentenced to death and placed in irons to await execution.

Several days later a temple attendant entered a jeweler's shop in the same city and offered a golden chain for sale. The jeweler was immediately suspicious, and reported the fact to the temple authorities who had the attendant arrested. As suspected, the chain was found to belong to the missing vase. The attendant confessed that he had stolen the vase and removed the chain, before burying the vase in the temple courtyard.

Again they dug up the courtyard, and this time they found the golden vase. It was located at the exact spot previously indicated by the cook, but it had been necessary to dig a few inches deeper.

We might ask: If the police had found the golden vase the first time, or if the real thief had not been apprehended, how would the cook have escaped execution? *Even if he had had a thousand mouths*, how would he have been able to prove his innocence?

27

A BROTHER'S DEVOTION

THE FATHER of two sons died suddenly without having made a will, and the elder son Hai, took the entire property for himself, leaving his younger brother Ba, only a miserable hut and a piece of arid land.

Ba spent most of his time working and plowing for Hai. In return, he was privileged to use Hai's buffaloes and plow, to till his own small field. But the fields of the elder brother grew greener and more flourishing every day, whereas those of the younger brother produced very little, and it was only with great difficulty that he kept from starving.

Although Hai was unfair and severe towards his own brother, he was most kind and generous to his many friends. He would receive them magnificently and help them on any and all occasions. Should one of them find himself in trouble for any reason, he was certain that he would not knock in vain at Hai's door. Hai even anticipated their desires.

Now it happened that Hai had a good-hearted and sensible wife, who did not approve of his conduct towards his younger brother.

"My dear husband," she would say to him, "why are you kinder to your friends than to your own brother? Does he not deserve your help and support?"

To this query, Hai would respond:

"He is old enough to look out for himself. If I help him, he will not know how to stand on his own and will keep on relying on me. Let him manage for himself.

"Moreover," he would add, "my friends are excellent people who are entirely devoted to me, and I like to return their civility and generosity."

These weak explanations never satisfied the wife, and she would reply:

"Still, brothers are of the same blood, and blood is always thicker than water. Friends at best may be aimiable egoists, parasites or flatterers, until they have proved themselves. I am quite convinced that in an emergency, you would find in your own brother, love, devotion, and help, whereas your friends would desert or betray you."

But Hai paid no attention to her arguments,

Ba knew his sister-in-law's sentiments and frequently visited his brother's home, even beyond the anniversaries and festivals at which his presence was required. But he never let the least bitterness or resentment toards Hai show, because he did not wish to sadden his sister-in-law. As for the latter, she did not dare offer him assistance, nor to defend him openly, for fear of wounding his pride. But she continued to hope that some day her husband would change his attitude.

*　　*　　*

One evening Hai returned home from work and found his wife in tears.

"What is wrong?" he asked.

"Alas! A great misfortune has befallen us," she sobbed. "While you were away at work a young beggar came to the door and asked for alms. I was busy in the kitchen and asked him to wait a moment. Seeing that the room was empty, he came in and stole some clothing. I surprised him in the act and in my anger hit him with a bamboo pole. He fell to the floor and struck his head against the bed, which killed him instantly. I then wrapped his body in a mat and carried it into the garden. Now I am frightened and don't know what to do."

Hai was more frightened than his wife and did not not know what to do either. Then his wife added:

"We are not on good terms with the mandarin. I did not kill the beggar on purpose, but if I confess, who knows how he will decide. It would mean ruin."

The husband became even more distraught at these remarks. Then she said to him:

"The beggar is dead. If we could bury him secretly in the forest, no one would ever know. Choose the most reliable or your friends to help you. You have been so generous with them that they will not refuse to give proof of their gratitude and devotion."

*   *   *

Reassured and full of hope, Hai went to the home of a very dear friend who opened the door with a broad smile. But as soon as Hai explained what had happened and asked for his help, the friend changed his demeanor and expressed his regrets: he was too old, too weak, he did not know how to carry a heavy load, he would only hinder him, etc. Hai should ask another, healthier friend.

Hai then ran to the home of another friend who was extremely happy to see him. He was warmly received and invited to take a cup of tea. The friend asked:

"What can I do for you, dear Hai? You look very upset and I shall be glad to do anything to relieve your worries. Tell me to jump into fire for your sake and I would do it without hesitation, for you know very well that my life is yours."

Hai heaved a great sigh of relief thinking that his misfortune would end there and that at last he had found the true and devoted friend he was looking for. But after he had finished his story and asked for help, the man suddenly remembered that his mother-in-law was seriously ill and he had to look after her. But he fully sympathized with Hai and said he was very sorry that he could not help.

The third friend to whom the unfortunate Hai applied, was struck by his serious mein and said to him before he could open his mouth:

A BROTHER'S DEVOTION

"What troubles you? Tell me about it. Between you and me there are no secrets."

Thinking himself saved at last and overcome with joy and gratefulness, Hai confided in his friend. Alas! This friend had a good reason why he could not accompany him. "But that does not prevent me from sharing your woes and of being sorry for you with all my heart," he said.

Hai knocked in vain at other doors. He then understood that those on whom he had called first, had had time to warn the others. Every door was closed. In the end, completely exhausted, he dragged himself home, half-dead with fear and despair.

* * *

Hai's wife gave him a tonic to renew his strength, and then he told her all that had happened. She said:

"It is getting late. You must go and ask your own brother Ba to come here. Please hurry, for there is no time to lose."

Hai hesitated for a moment, but he no longer had a will of his own. He went immediately to his younger brother's hut. Ba was surprised to see him there, especially since it was late at night.

"How pale you are," he said. "Are you ill, or is your wife ill?"

When he learned the truth, Ba showed himself to be a most loving and devoted brother and offered his help without a second's hesitation. He went at once to help Hai bury the beggar, and did all he could to comfort his elder brother.

When they had completed the task it was long past midnight, and Hai was at the end of his strength. It was almost dawn before the brothers returned home.

*　　*　　*

Next morning Hai and his wife were summoned to the mandarin's home without delay. Ba was also summoned.

When they arrived there they found all those friends of whom Hai had solicited aid. Each one pointed an accusing finger at them and gave their testimony. The two brothers knew then that their denunciators had followed them into the forest the evening before. The mandarin said in a solemn voice:

"You have committed murder, and furthermore you have secretly buried the body. You have even had the audacity to ask these citizens to become your accomplices. Fortunately they are honest men, who obey the voice of their consciences. It is useless for you to deny your foul deed. Lead us at once to the place where you have buried the man, and let justice be done."

Everyone went to the forest and the grave was opened. But great was their suprise when the mat was unrolled, and instead of the body of a beggar, it was found to contain the corpse of a big black dog.

The mandarin knitted his brows, and the accusers could not hide their chagrin. Hai and Ba did not know what to think, but they had to congratulate themselves at the turn of events. Then Hai's wife prostrated herself before the mandarin and begged permission to speak. When permission was granted she said:

A BROTHER'S DEVOTION

"I knew that my husband loved his friends more than his own brother, and for a long time I have been trying to think of a way to open his eyes. I wanted especially to prove to him that brotherly love is deep and holy. Yesterday, during my husband's absence, my dog died. I made up the entire story to help my husband find out the truth about his friends. And this is the result, O most righteous magistrate."

Each of the friends, who stood there dumbfounded and crestfallen, was sentenced to receive fifty lashes. It is hard to imagine how they could ever hope to look Hai in the face again. Hai fell sobbing on his brother's shoulder in a show of uncontrolled emotion.

From that time on Hai and Ba lived like true brothers and shared every joy and sorrow with each other. This was greatly pleasing to Hai's good wife, whose clever trick had brought them together again.

28

THE STORY OF TAM AND CAM

ONCE UPON a time there lived a man and his wife and their little daughter, Tam. They were good people and lived a happy life until the wife died. After several years, he married again, but the second wife was a wicked woman.

On the first day after the wedding, when there was a big banquet in the house, little Tam was shut up in a room, instead of being allowed to help welcome the guests and attend the feast. Moreover, she was sent to bed without any supper.

Things grew worse when a new baby girl was born. The new child was named Cam, and it was adored by both parents. Poor Tam was now in a worse situation than before, and the stepmother told her husband so many lies about her that he refused to have anything to do with his own daughter.

"Stay in the kitchen and do not annoy us, you naughty child," the wicked stepmother would say.

She gave the little girl a dirty wretched place in the kitchen, and it was there that she had to live and work. At night she slept on a torn mat and had only a ragged sheet as coverlet. Tam was forced to scrub the floors, cut the wood, feed the animals, and do the cooking, washing, and many other tasks. Large blisters formed on her soft little hands, but she bore the pain without complaint. Her stepmother would often send her into the deep forest to gather wood in the secret hope that some wild beast would carry her off. She asked Tam to draw water from wells which were dangerously deep, hoping that she would fall in and drown.

Tam worked so hard that her skin became darkened with dirt and grease, and her hair became matted and scraggly. Whenever she went to the well to draw water, she would look at her image and it frightened her to realize how dirty and ugly she had become. She took some water in the palm of her hand, washed her face, combed her long, smooth hair with her fingers, and the soft white skin appeared again.

When the evil stepmother realized how pretty Tam could look, she hated her more than ever and wished to do her more harm. One day she told Tam and her own daughter, Cam, to go fishing in the village pond.

"Try to catch a lot of fish," she said, "if you come back with only a few, you will be whipped, and sent to bed without your supper."

Tam knew that these words were meant for her, for the stepmother would never think of beating Cam, who was the apple of her eye. But Tam was now used to hard whippings.

Tam fished diligently, and by the end of the day she had a basketful of fish. On the other hand, Cam spent the day rolling in the tender grass, picking wild flowers, basking in the sun, and dancing and singing. The sun had set before Cam even began to fish. She looked at Tam's full basket and then at her own, which was empty. An idea came to her.

"Sister, sister," she cried, "your hair is full of mud. Why don't you wade into the fresh water and wash your hair. Otherwise, mother is going to scold you."

Tam listened to this advice, and swam out into the water to wash her hair. Meanwhile Cam emptied Tam's fish into her own basket, and ran home.

When Tam returned to the shore and realized that her fish had been stolen, her heart sank, and she began to cry bitterly. She was certain her stepmother would punish her severely.

Suddenly a fresh and balmy wind arose, the sky became clear and the clouds whiter, and she saw in front of her the smiling, blue-robed Goddess of Mercy, carrying a green willow branch.

"What is the matter, dear child?" the Goddess asked in a sweet, pure voice.

Tam related all that had happened and added:

"Most Noble Lady, what am I to do tonight when I

return home? I am very frightened, for my stepmother will not believe that the fish were stolen. She will whip me very, very hard."

The Goddess of Mercy consoled her:

"Your misfortunes will soon be over. Have confidence in me and be of good cheer. Now look in your basket to see whether there is anything left."

Tam looked in the basket and saw a lovely little fish with red fins and golden eyes. She uttered a cry of surprise.

The Goddess told her to take the fish home, put it in the well at the rear of the house, and feed it three times a day with what she could save from her own food.

Tam thanked the Goddess gratefully and did exactly as she had been told. Whenever she went to the well, the fish would appear on the surface to greet her, but never showed itself to anyone else.

The stepmother noticed Tam's strange actions and began to spy on her. She went to the well to look for the fish, but it was hidden in deep water. She then plotted against Tam. One day she ordered her to go to a distant spring to fetch water, and taking advantage of her absence, disguised herself in Tam's ragged clothes and went to the well. She called the fish, and when it came to the surface, scooped it up with a net, and ate it for supper.

When Tam returned home, she went at once to the well and called and called, but the golden fish did not appear. Then she noticed that the surface of the water was stained with blood and realized the truth. Tam leaned her head against the well and wept miserably.

The Goddess of Mercy appeared to her again, and with a face as sweet as that of a loving and compassionate mother, she comforted the child.

"Do not cry," she said. "Your stepmother has killed the fish and eaten it, but you must find the bones and bury them in the ground under your mat. Pray to them and whatever you may wish for will be granted."

Tam followed the Goddess' instructions and began to search for the fish's bones, but could find no trace.

"Cluck! Cluck!" said a hen. "Give me some rice, and I will show you where the bones are hidden."

Tam gave her a handful of rice and the hen said:

"Cluck! Cluck! Follow me."

When she came to the poultry yard, the hen scratched in a dunghill and uncovered the fish's bones. Tam gathered them up and reburied them as she had been told. It was not long before she received gold and jewelry, and dresses of such wonderful materials they would have rejoiced the heart of any young girl.

Soon it came time for the Autumn Festival, but Tam was ordered to stay at home and sort out two big baskets of black and green beans that the wicked stepmother had purposely mixed together.

"When you have finished your work," she said, "you may go to the festival, but not before."

Then the stepmother and Cam put on thir most beautiful dresses and went out. When they had been gone for some time, Tam lifted her tearful face to heaven and prayed:

"O Benevolent Goddess of Mercy, please help me."

The soft-eyed Goddess appeared at once. With her magic green willow branch, she turned the little flies into sparrows, which sorted the beans for the girl. Tam dried her tears, dressed herself in a glittering, blue-and-silver gown, and went to the festival.

Cam was greatly surprised to see her half-sister at the festival, and whispered to her mother:

"That rich lady is strangely like my sister Tam?"

When Tam realized that her stepmother and Cam were staring at her, she ran away in such a hurry she lost one of her fine slippers.

A court noble discovered the slipper and presented it to the king.

The king examined the slipper carefully and declared he had never before seen such a work of art. He asked the ladies of the Court to try it on, but the slipper was too small for even the smallest foot among the noble ladies. Then he sent messengers throughout the kingdom with orders for all women everywhere to try on the slipper; but it would fit none of them. Finally, word was sent out that the woman whose foot could fit the slipper, would become his queen.

Finally it was Tam's turn to try the slipper. It fitted her foot perfectly. She then appeared in Court wearing both slippers and her glittering glue-and-silver gown, looking extremely beautiful. She was married to the king at a big wedding attended by many dignitaries, and thenceforth led a brilliant and happy life.

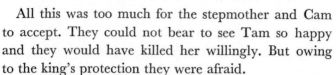

All this was too much for the stepmother and Cam to accept. They could not bear to see Tam so happy and they would have killed her willingly. But owing to the king's protection they were afraid.

On her father's name's day, Tam returned home to celebrate with her family. At that time, however great and important one might be, one was always expected by one's parents to behave exactly like a young and obedient child. The cunning stepmother took advantage of this custom, and asked Tam to climb an areca tree to obtain some nuts for the guests. As Tam was queen, she could have refused, but she was a very pious and dutiful daughter, so climbed the tree. While there, she felt it swaying to and fro in a strange and alarming manner.

"What are you doing?" she asked her stepmother.

"I am only trying to frighten the ants, which might bite you my dear child," came the reply.

But in fact, the wicked stepmother had obtained an axe, and she cut down the tree, which fell with a crash. Poor Tam was killed instantly.

"Now we are rid of her," said the horrid woman, with an ugly laugh. "She will never come back. We shall report to the king that she died in an accident, and my beloved daughter, Cam, will become queen in her stead!"

THE STORY OF TAM AND CAM

Things happened exactly as she had planned, and Cam became the king's wife.

But Tam's pure and innocent soul could find no rest. She was turned into a nightingale, living in a beautiful grove near the king's garden.

One day, one of the palace maids was airing the king's dragon-embroidered robe, and the nightingale sang in her melodious voice:

"O sweet maid, be careful with my husband's robe and do not tear it by putting it on a thorny hedge."

The nightingale sang so sweetly she moved the hearts of all who heard her. Even the king was attracted by her voice. She sang so sadly that tears came into his eyes. At last the king said:

"Delightful nightingale, if you are the soul of my beloved queen, be pleased to settle in my wide sleeves."

The gentle bird went straight into the king's sleeves, and rubbed her smooth head against his hand.

She was then put in a golden cage in the king's bedroom. The king became so fond of her that he would stay near the cage all day listening to her beautiful melancholic songs.

Cam became jealous of the nightingale and sought her mother's advice. One day, while the king was holding a council with his ministers, Cam killed the bird, and threw the feathers into the royal gardens.

"What is the meaning of this?" asked the king, when he saw the empty cage.

There was great confusion in the palace. Everyone looked for the nightingale, but no one could find it.

"Perhaps she was bored and flew off," said Cam.

The king was very sad, but there was nothing he could do about it, other than resign himself to fate.

Once again, however, Tam's restless soul was transformed. This time it became a great, magnificent tree. It bore only a single fruit, but what a wonderful fruit it was! It was perfectly round, large, and had a very sweet smell. An old woman passing by the tree and seeing the beautiful fruit, said:

151

"Golden fruit, golden fruit,
"Drop into the bag of this old woman.
"This one will never eat you.
"She will keep you and enjoy your beauty."

The fruit at once dropped into the old woman's bag. She took it home to enjoy its appearance and fragrant smell. But the next day, on returning from some errands, to her great surprise she found her house clean and tidy, and a delicious hot meal waiting for her. It was as if some magic hand had done this during her absence.

The following morning the old woman pretended to go out, but she returned stealthily, and watched the house. Soon she beheld a fair and slender lady coming out of the golden fruit. She was even more surprised when the lady began to tidy up the house. The old woman rushed into the room and tore away the peel, so that the fair lady could no longer hide herself within the fruit. The young lady then had to remain in the house and consider the old woman as her mother.

One day the king went hunting and became lost.

He saw the old woman's house and asked for shelter. According to custom, the latter offered him some tea and betel. The king observed the delicate way in which the betel had been prepared and asked:

"Who made this betel? It looks exactly like that prepared by my late beloved queen."

In a trembling voice, the old woman replied: "Son of Heaven, it was made by my unworthy daughter."

The king then ordered the daughter to be brought before him. When she came in, she bowed low, and he immediately realized that it was Tam, his beloved queen. They both wept bitter tears after such a long separation and so much unhappiness. Tam then returned to the capital with the king, where she took her rightful place as first wife and queen.

Cam was completely forgotten by the king.

She then thought to herself: "If I were as beautiful as my sister, I would win the king's heart." She asked the queen: "Dearest sister, how can my skin become as white as yours?"

"It is very simple," answered the queen, who was now completely aware of Cam's ill-will, "you have only to jump into a vat of boiling water."

Cam believed her and did as she was told.

This was the end of Cam, and she died instantly.

When the wicked stepmother learned of Cam's death, she wept so long that she became blind, and shortly after, died of a broken heart.

Queen Tam was now free of her enemies, and lived the rest of her life in peace and happiness.

VIETNAMESE LEGENDS

29

THE GENTLEMAN OF THE FLIES

THERE ONCE lived a gentleman who was very handsome and well-educated. He was pleased to lead an easy life, unburdened by routine cares and tribulations. He had a very easy-going nature, and he had never been known to harm any living creature.

He was particularly generous with the flies who invaded his house. He served them many delicious meals and instructed his servants to set food apart for them. The flies appreciated this consideration and returned his affection. They guarded him carefully, and saw to it that neither mosquitoes nor any other insects disturbed his sleep.

The king of the country in which the gentleman lived, was seeking a husband for his daughter, a princess renowned for her great beauty and talent. The king wanted a man endowed with superior intelligence, who would also be kind and handsome.

For a long time he considered how to find a proper husband. Finally he decided on a plan.

154

The king had a secret palace built far away from the capital. Inside the palace were nine identical rooms, all of which were kept locked. The princess was installed in one of the rooms of this secret palace, and the king decreed that the suitor who could guess in which room the princess lived, would be accepted as her future husband.

The young men of the country were eager to enter the contest, for they all considered themselves handsome and intelligent. But each failed in turn. When they failed—and this was a part of the conditions for entering the contest—they received twenty strokes by a cane. Over a hundred contestants were unsucessful, and others became wary, for they did not look forward to the caning or to the ridicule of failure.

Our gentleman wished to marry the princess very much, and in his preoccupation to solve the problem, forgot to feed the flies.

The flies understood the reason behind his behaviour and decided to help him. They flew unobserved into the palace, discovered the princess, and reported back to their friend.

With this valuable information, the gentleman walked into the palace, and nonchalantly indicated the correct chamber.

The king was unable to believe the puzzle had been solved, and decided on a further test.

This time, nine meals were served on nine identical tables, with one table bearing the suitor's name, secretly hidden under a food platter. The problem was to select the correct table.

For several days the gentleman walked around the tables without finding a clue to the situation.

But once again the flies came to his aid. They had seen where his name had been placed, and generously passed on the solution.

Confidently he went to the king and gave him the correct answer. The king was then compelled to concede defeat, and he graciously gave him the princess in marriage. The couple lived happily ever after.

When the story of the gentleman's secret alliance with the flies became known, the people nicknamed him "Gentleman of the Flies." Fortunately his wife never heard of this nickname, and when he died the flies lost their one and only friend.

30

IN SEARCH OF
A FREE MEAL

THERE WAS once a man whose principal occupation was to make an appearance whenever a bountiful meal was to be served. He would make it seem that he had arrived to settle some important matter, but actually he was only interested in the food that was set before him.

A neighbor who had observed this behavior for some time decided to teach him a leasson. He told his wife to go to the city market, and buy meats and others foodstuffs in sufficient quantity for a large banquet.

Our man chanced to meet the neighbor's wife in the street and noticed she was carrying a large basket on her arm. He properly surmised that she was going to market to buy food for a considerable meal.

At the proper hour he called at the house on a pretext, and was invited to join the banquet.

Just as the servants were bringing in the first dishes, the master of the house winked at his wife. This was the signal for her to pretend to be seized with colic. She threw herself into a fit and moaned with pain.

The meal was served, but the guests left the table in search of a remedy for the stricken hostess. Our man, who was also greatly troubled, asked the husband what could be done.

"What a misfortune!" said the host, running his hand through his hair. "And to think that I myself sent her off to the market today! There is only one cure for her affliction, and that is some blood from the nose".

Our man saw that the food on the table was growing cold and some action had to be taken quickly to save the situation.

"Well," he said, "tell your servant to bring me a cloth and I will see that you get the necessary blood!"

He then clenched his fist and struck himself on the nose, which began to bleed profusely. After applying the cloth to absorb some blood, he handed it to his hostess with the hopes of an immediate cure, so they could begin eating.

While waiting for the meal to commence, his nose began swell until it had reached enormous proportions. Also the pain was so intense that the poor man was in agony.

At this point the master of the house reported that his wife had recovered, and the banquet could continue. But the man was in such pain, he had to decline the invitation, and return home.

IN SEARCH OF A FREE MEAL

So the self-inflicted nosebleed, which he thought would provide him with an excellent dinner, forced him to return home with an empty stomach, and a nose so painfully battered that he had lost his appetite!

31

THE BLIND SON-IN-LAW

THERE WAS once a handsome young man who had been blind from birth, but because his eyes looked quite normal, very few people were aware of his affliction.

One day he went to the home of a young lady to ask her parents for her hand in marriage. The men of the household were about to go out to work in the rice fields, and in order to demonstrate his industry, he decided to join them. He trailed along behind the others and was able to do his share of the day's work. When it came time to finish for the day all the men hurried homeward for the evening meal. But the blind man lost contact with the others and fell into a well.

When the guest did not appear, the future mother-in-law said: "Oh, that fellow will be a fine son-in-law for he puts in a full day's labor. But it is really time for him to stop for today. Boys, run out to the field and tell him to return for supper."

The men grumbled at this task but set out and looked for him. As they passed the well, the blind man overheard their conversation and was able to clamber out and follow them back to the house.

At the meal, the blind man was seated next to his future mother-in-law, who loaded his plate with food.

But then disaster struck. A bold dog approached, and began to eat the food from his plate.

"Why don't you give that dog a good slap?" asked his future mother-in-law. "Why do you let him eat your food?"

"Madam," replied the blind man, "I have too much respect for the master and the mistress of this house, to dare strike their dog."

"No matter," replied the worthy lady. "Here is a mallet; if that dog dares bother you again, give him a good blow on the head."

Now the mother-in-law saw that the young man was so modest and shy that he seemed afraid to eat, and would take nothing from his plate, She wanted to encourage him and selected some sweetmeats from a large platter and placed them before him.

On hearing the clatter of the chopsticks against his plate, the blind man thought that the dog had returned to annoy him, so he took up the mallet and gave the poor woman such a fierce blow on the head that she fell unconscious.

Needless to say that was the end of his courtship!

VIETNAMESE LEGENDS

32

EAGER FOR PUNISHMENT

THERE WAS once a beautiful and virtuous lady who made up her mind to marry only a wealthy and distinguished gentleman.

She left her father's home, built a residence for herself, and took up a life of pleasant idleness.

Among those who fell prey to her charms were the mayor of the town, the chief bonze of the pagoda, and even the district prefect. These three began to call at her home with great regularity. But in her opinion these people did not amount to very much, and since they were taking up a great deal of her time, she decided to teach them a lesson.

One day the young lady invited the chief bonze to spend the evening at her home; on the same day she invited the mayor and the prefect to come there during the third watch.

The chief bonze was the first to arrive. He had hardly finished his tea when there was a knock on the door.

"Hey there inside! Please open the door."

With that the chief bonze was seized with fear, for he had recognized the mayor's voice. He was deathly afraid that the people of the village would find out that he had neglected his religious duties, to pay court to a young woman.

It was a very embarrassing situation.

"What shall I do?" he asked. The young lady told him to hide in a dark corner of the room.

She then went to the door and admitted the mayor.

"You have invited me to come here this evening," he said. "Is there some important matter that you wish to discuss with me?"

"Yes," she replied, "as a matter of fact, there is something on my mind."

When she had offered the mayor betel, and he had smoked a cigarette and finished his tea, the young lady asked the following question:

"I am a poor orphan," she said, "and have no experience in the world and do not know anything about the law. Please tell me, Your Honor, how would you punish a bonze who leaves his pagoda at night to seduce defenseless women?"

The mayor replied with great vehemence: "These bonzes are exempt from all communal labor and they steal our tax money. If what you say is true the culprit should be beheaded immediately!"

VIETNAMESE LEGENDS

The mayor had hardly pronounced these words when a knock was heard at the door.

"Is anyone there? It is the prefect."

At the word "prefect," the mayor ran to hide in a corner of the room.

The young lady then opened the door and admitted the caller.

When he had had his fill of tea and sweetmeats, he sat back and asked the lady of the house how he might be of service to her, and why she had invited him to call on that particular evening.

To this question the young lady arose and said: "Your Excellency, I am only a woman and I have had no experience with the law. I beg you to advise me on a certain matter. How would the law punish a bonze who leaves his pagoda at night to pay court to the young ladies of the neighborhood?"

The prefect hesitated for a moment and then replied with great certainty: "If one of these bonzes has done as you have said, he should receive fifty lashes on his bare back, and be compelled to take part in the communal work of the town with the other people."

The chief bonze was gnawing his lip in despair, but when he heard the words of the prefect, he jumped up from his corner and fell prone at the latter's feet.

"Your Excellency!" he cried. You have judged properly. I will accept your punishment. But the mayor, who is hiding over there in the corner, wants to behead me. Truly you are the one who interprets the law correctly!"

EAGER FOR PUNISHMENT